Quaderno di laboratorio

Basic Conversational ITALIAN 2nd Edition

Cecilia Bartoli Pina Swenson

HOLT, RINEHART AND WINSTON
New York San Francisco Toronto London

ISBN: 0-03-021686-9

Printed in the United States of America

9012 140 987654321

Table of Contents

Introduction

This Quaderno d'esercizi per il laboratorio accompanies Basic Conversational Italian, Second Edition, and is designed to provide additional oral and written practice of the material presented in the text.

Each Unit of the Quaderno is divided into Part One and Part Two. There are two laboratory sessions per Unit, each approximately twenty minutes in length, and each Part is a guide to the corresponding laboratory session. Since the laboratory sessions provide both oral and written practice, we suggest that the students keep the Quaderno open to the correct page at all times.

Part One of each Unit consists of a "mini-dialogue" (new material in Units 1-4, in subsequent Units a short segment of one of the two dialogues found in the text) that the students will repeat sentence by sentence for pronunciation practice. The remainder of Part One is devoted to oral practice of grammatical constructions.

Part Two consists of five sections: (1) additional grammar practice; (2) a reading of one of the dialogues in the corresponding chapter of the main text, followed by multiple choice comprehension questions; (3) intonation practice and sound discrimination; (4) pronunciation practice, focusing on one vowel or consonant sound at a time; (5) dictation.

The Quaderno d'esercizi per il laboratorio contains the directions in English for all the exercises found on tape as well as an example for each exercise. Space has been provided for students to write the responses when a written response is called for. A broken line (......) indicates that an oral response is required; a solid line (______) calls for a written response.

All the grammar exercises, except for the simple substitution drills, are four-phased--the student is asked to repeat the correct response for added reinforcement. Throughout, the grammar points are presented in the same order and under the same headings as in the main text.

The intonation exercises provide additional practice in the intonation or "melody" of whole Italian phrases and sentences, while stressing discrimination between similar-sounding words and forms, and between different types of sentence such as questions, commands, and statements of fact.

The pronunciation sections focus on one or two Italian sounds per section, and thus give the student an opportunity to practice each Italian sound in the context of real words, phrases, and sentences. The exercises require the students to repeat after the speaker, pronouncing two similar sounds and making the distinction between them. At the same time, students make the connection between the spoken and the written word. This section includes dictation of new words containing the sound being studied.

The dictation consists of complete sentences--five or six of them--using known vocabulary. This tests the students' mastery of vocabulary, grammar, and spelling.

Through working with whole sentences, questions, and expressions, students become accustomed to speaking smoothly, in complete phrases. Grammar, pronunciation, and expression are integrated and reinforced while the student's confidence builds.

We have tried to make this Quaderno and the accompanying lab sessions as enjoyable as possible. We hope that the students will enjoy their lab sessions with this program.

— C. B.

— P. S.

NAME ______________________ DATE ____________ CLASS ____________

UNIT 1

Part One

DIALOGUE

Listen to the following dialogue.

Laura: Buon giorno. Casa Fini?
Signora Fini: Sí, qui parla la signora Fini. Con chi parlo?
Laura: Sono Laura, l'amica di Anna. Come sta signora?
Signora Fini: Bene grazie e Lei?
Laura: Benissimo. Anna è a casa?
Signora Fini: No, non c'è.
Laura: Grazie e arrivederLa.

Now repeat each sentence after the speaker.

GRAMMATICA

I. GENDER AND NUMBER OF NOUNS. THE DEFINITE ARTICLE.

A. *Create new sentences by substituting in the base sentence the words given.*

1. Example: La casa è qui.
telefono
Il telefono è qui.

....

....

2. Example: Le case sono qui.
telefoni
I telefoni sono qui.

....

....

3. Example: Io sono lo zio di Giacomo.
   amico
   Io sono l'amico di Giacomo.

   ....

   ....

B. *Complete the following expressions by supplying the appropriate definite article. Then repeat the correct sentence after the speaker gives it.*

   Example: medici sono a casa
   I medici sono a casa.

   1. .... 4. ....

   2. .... 5. ....

   3. ....

II. THE PRESENT TENSE OF *ESSERE* AND *STARE*

A. *Create new sentences by substituting in the base sentence the word or phrase given. Change the verb accordingly.*

   1. Example: Il medico è in Italia.
      i medici
      I medici sono in Italia.

      ....

      ....

   2. Example: Gli studenti sono a casa
      lei
      È a casa.

      ....

      ....

   3. Example: L'amico di Giacomo è qui.
      gli zii
      Gli zii di Giacomo sono qui.

      ....

      ....

NAME ______________________________ DATE ____________ CLASS ____________

B. *Change the following sentences from singular to plural. Then repeat the correct sentence after the speaker gives it.*

Example: L'amica è a casa.
Le amiche sono a casa.

1. .... 5. ....

2. .... 6. ....

3. .... 7. ....

4. .... 8. ....

C. *Create new sentences by substituting in the base sentence the word or phrase given.*

1. Example: Il telefono sta qui.
la casa
La casa sta qui.

....

....

2. Example: Lo zio sta bene.
tu
Stai bene.

....

....

NAME ______________________ DATE __________ CLASS __________

UNIT 1

Part Two

GRAMMATICA

II. PRESENT TENSE OF *ESSERE* AND *STARE*, CONTINUED

A. *Answer the following questions as in the example. Then repeat the correct sentence after the speaker gives it.*

Example: Come stanno le studentesse?
Le studentesse stanno bene, grazie.

1. ....
2. ....
3. ....
4. ....
5. ....

Example: Sono qui le signorine?
Sì, le signorine stanno qui.

1. ....
2. ....
3. ....
4. ....
5. ....

B. *Change the following sentences from singular to plural. Then repeat the correct sentence after the speaker gives it.*

Example: La riga sta qui.
Le righe stanno qui.

1. ....
2. ....
3. ....
4. ....
5. ....
6. ....

Example: La signora è a casa.
Le signore sono a casa.

1. .... 4. ....

2. .... 5. ....

3. .... 6. ....

L I S T E N I N G / C O M P R E H E N S I O N

Listen to the following dialogue.

UNA TELEFONATA

Laura Ritter è una studentessa americana. Ora è in Italia. Laura telefona a casa di un amico, Giacomo Fini, un giovane italiano.

Signor Fini: Pronto? Chi parla?
Laura: Pronto. Casa Fini?
Signor Fini: Sì, qui casa Fini. Con chi parlo?
Laura: Sono Laura Ritter, un'amica di Giacomo.
Signor Fini: Buon giorno, signorina. Io sono lo zio di Giacomo. Come sta?
Laura: Sto bene, grazie, e Lei?
Signor Fini: Non c'è male, grazie. Che cosa desidera?
Laura: Giacomo è a casa?
Signor Fini: No. Giacomo non c'è ora. È a lezione d'inglese.
Laura: Peccato! Allora telefono più tardi.
Signor Fini: Benissimo. ArrivederLa, signorina.
Laura: ArrivederLa, signor Fini. Mi saluti la signora Fini.
Signor Fini: Grazie, buon giorno.

QUESTIONS

You will hear five questions about the dialogue you have just heard. Indicate the correct answer to each question by circling the letter before it. You will hear each question twice.

1. ....

a. una studentessa italiana

b. un'amica di Giacomo

c. una signorina inglese

NAME ______________________ DATE ____________ CLASS ____________

2. ....

a. Sí, è a casa.

b. No, è a casa di un amico.

c. No, è a lezione d'inglese.

3. ....

a. con Giacomo

b. con la signora Fini

c. con lo zio di Giacomo

4. ....

a. benissimo

b. non c'è male

c. bene

5. ....

a. No, è a casa di un amico.

b. Sí, è in Italia.

c. No, è a casa Fini.

INTONATION AND SOUND DISCRIMINATION

A. *Change the following statements into questions by changing the intonation. Repeat the questions, imitating the speaker, during the second pause.*

Example: È una studentessa americana
È una studentessa americana?

1. ....
2. ....
3. ....
4. ....
5. ....
6. ....
7. ....

B. *Listen to the following sentences and tell whether you hear a statement of fact or a question: circle S if you hear a statement, Q if you hear a question. You will hear each statement or question twice.*

1. .... S Q
2. .... S Q
3. .... S Q
4. .... S Q
5. .... S Q
6. .... S Q

C. *Listen to the following statements and tell whether they are in the singular or plural: circle S if singular, P if plural. You will hear each sentence twice.*

1. .... S P
2. .... S P
3. .... S P
4. .... S P
5. .... S P
6. .... S P
7. .... S P
8. .... S P

D. *Listen to the following short sentences using* essere *and* stare. *Repeat each, then circle the subject of the verb during the pause. You will hear each sentence twice.*

1. .... io tu lei/lui noi voi loro
2. .... io tu lei/lui noi voi loro
3. .... io tu lei/lui noi voi loro
4. .... io tu lei/lui noi voi loro
5. .... io tu lei/lui noi voi loro
6. .... io tu lei/lui noi voi loro
7. .... io tu lei/lui noi voi loro
8. .... io tu lei/lui noi voi loro
9. .... io tu lei/lui noi voi loro
10. .... io tu lei/lui noi voi loro
11. .... io tu lei/lui noi voi loro
12. .... io tu lei/lui noi voi loro

NAME ______________________________ DATE ___________ CLASS ____________

P R O N U N C I A T I O N

A. *Italian has seven vowel sounds, two semi-vowels and twenty consonant sounds. In Italian the semi-vowels and all the consonant sounds except /ñ/, /l̃/, and /r/ are similar to the corresponding English sounds. Of the Italian vowels, the following have similar--but not identical--sounds in English. Practice them, noticing the subtle differences.*

/i/ fini, lini, tini, mi, ti, pini, stili, vini, fili, stinti, i

/ / è, lei, festa, lesti, geli, gelidi, desti, sei, vesti, cento, beni, c'è

/a/ tana, lana, sana, sala, papa, fa, canta, data, vana, manti, santa, sta

/ / ho, poi, so, dò, toni, modi, vostri, nota, nostri, coni, doti, sto

/u/ tu, lui, luna, tuta, funi, matura, saluta, muti, tutela

B. *Practice these sounds in phrases. Repeat each phrase during the pause.*

1. vini finissimi tipici tini piccini
2. vestiti lesti la festa della messe
3. Anna fa la nanna le braccie della mamma
4. portami un po' d'olio cotto da un soldo
5. muta è la luna lassú nel cielo blu

D I C T A T I O N

Listen to the following sentences. Then write each sentence during the pause. Each sentence will be repeated so that you can check your accuracy.

1. ____

2. ____

3. ____

4. ____

5. ____

NAME ______________________________ DATE ____________ CLASS ____________

UNIT 2

Part One

D I A L O G U E

Listen to the following dialogue.

Anna, una studentessa italiana, telefona a un'amica.

Anna: Ciao Maria, come stai?
Maria: Bene e tu?
Anna: Benissimo grazie.
Maria: Dove sei?
Anna: A lezione d'inglese.
Maria: Perché non ci vediamo?
Anna: D'accordo, ci vediamo al solito bar.
Maria: A fra poco.

Now repeat each sentence after the speaker.

G R A M M A T I C A

I. NEGATIVES, INTERROGATIVES: *NON, NESSUNO, CHI, DOVE, COME*

A. *Change the following sentences from the affirmative to the negative. Then repeat the correct sentence after the speaker gives it.*

1. Example: Stanno bene.
Non stanno bene.

1. .... 4. ....

2. .... 5. ....

3. .... 6. ....

2. Example: Gli ospiti stanno bene.
Gli ospiti non stanno bene.

1. .... 4. ....

2. .... 5. ....

3. .... 6. ....

B. *Change the following sentences from the negative to the affirmative. Then repeat the correct sentence after the speaker gives it.*

Example: Giacomo non è a lezione d'inglese.
Giacomo è a lezione d'inglese.

1. .... 4. ....

2. .... 5. ....

3. ....

C. *Answer the following questions as in the example. Then repeat both question and correct answer after the speaker gives them.*

1. Example: Chi è qui?
Nessuno è qui.
Chi è qui? Nessuno è qui.

1. .... 4. ....

2. .... 5. ....

3. ....

2. Example: Dov'è Laura, in un bar?
No, Laura non è in un bar.
Dov'è Laura, in un bar? No, Laura non è in un bar.

1. .... 3. .... 5. ....

2. .... 4. ....

3. Example: Come sta lo zio di Giacomo?
Lo zio di Giacomo non sta bene.
Come sta lo zio di Giacomo? Lo zio di Giacomo non sta bene.

1. .... 4. ....

2. .... 5. ....

3. .... 6. ....

NAME ______________________________ DATE ___________ CLASS ____________

PLURAL OF MASCULINE NOUNS ENDING IN -A AND -ISTA

A. *Change the following sentences from singular to plural. Then repeat the correct sentence after the speaker gives it.*

1. Example: L'artista non è qui.
   Gli artisti non sono qui.

   1. ....   4. ....

   2. ....   5. ....

   3. ....

2. Example: Dov'è il problema?
   Dove sono i problemi?

   1. ....   3. ....

   2. ....   4. ....

B. *Create new questions and answers by substituting in the base the words given.*

1. Example: È qui lo zio? No, lo zio non è qui. (gli artisti)
   Sono qui gli artisti? No, gli artisti non sono qui.

   ....

   ....

2. Example: Dov'è l'amico? L'amico non sta qui. (i dentisti)
   Dove sono i dentisti? I dentisti non stanno qui.

   ....

   ....

C. *Make the following plural questions singular. Then answer them in the negative. Repeat the correct question and answer after the speaker gives them.*

Example: Sono qui gli artisti?
È qui l'artista? No, l'artista non è qui.

1. ....   3. ....

2. ....   4. ....

Example: Dove stanno le case?
Dove sta la casa? La casa non sta qui.

....

....

NAME ______________________ DATE __________ CLASS __________

UNIT 2

Part Two

GRAMMATICA

PRESENT TENSE OF *AVERE*

A. *Create new sentences by substituting in the base sentence the words given.*

1. Example: Gli ospiti hanno la febbre.
   Giacomo
   Giacomo ha la febbre.

   ....

   ....

2. Example: Che cosa ha l'artista?
   la zia
   Che cosa ha la zia?

   ....

   ....

B. *Change the following sentences from singular to plural. Then repeat the correct sentence after the speaker gives it.*

Example: L'artista sta a casa.
Gli artisti stanno a casa.

1. .... 4. ....

2. .... 5. ....

3. .... 6. ....

L I S T E N I N G / C O M P R E H E N S I O N

Listen to the following dialogue.

UN'ALTRA TELEFONATA

Laura compra un gettone e telefona un'altra volta a Giacomo.

Giacomo: Casa Fini.
Laura: Ah, ciao. Giacomo, sei tu?
Giacomo: Sí, sono io. Chi è? Laura? Dove sei?
Laura: Sono in un bar di via Veneto. Come stai?
Giacomo: Io, bene, e tu?
Laura: Anch'io, grazie. Voi state tutti bene?
Giacomo: Noi stiamo bene, ma gli ospiti inglesi stanno male.
Laura: Che cosa hanno?
Giacomo: Hanno la febbre. Forse è l'influenza.
Laura: Siete preoccupati?
Giacomo: Veramente no, ma sai com'è: gli stranieri vogliono subito andare all'ospedale, chiamare lo specialista e magari anche lo psichiatra.
Laura: Ma via, non scherzare!
Giacomo: Hai ragione. Nessuno è cosí esagerato.
Laura: Senti, perché non ci vediamo?
Giacomo: D'accordo. Sei al solito bar?
Laura: Sí.
Giacomo: A fra poco allora.
Laura: Ciao!

Q U E S T I O N S

You will hear five questions about the dialogue you have just heard. Indicate the correct answer to each question by circling the letter before it. You will hear each question twice.

1. ....

   a. un telefono

   b. un gettone

   c. un bar

2. ....

   a. a via Veneto

   b. all'ospedale

   c. a casa Fini

3. ....

   a. allo specialista

   b. allo psichiatra

   c. a Giacomo

4. ....

   a. benissimo

   b. bene

   c. male

NAME ________________ DATE __________ CLASS __________

5. ....

a. al bar

b. all'ospedale

c. a casa Fini

INTONATION AND SOUND DISCRIMINATION

A. *Repeat the following sentence expansions during each pause.*

a. noi stiamo bene
noi stiamo tutti bene, ma gli ospiti no
noi stiamo tutti bene, ma gli ospiti no, stanno male
noi stiamo tutti bene, ma gli ospiti inglesi no, stanno male

b. ci vediamo?
non ci vediamo?
perché non ci vediamo?
senti, perché non ci vediamo?

B. *Listen to the following questions and tell whether formal or informal address is used in each. During the pause, circle F if formal, I if informal. You will hear each question twice.*

1. .... F I
2. .... F I
3. .... F I
4. .... F I
5. .... F I
6. .... F I
7. .... F I
8. .... F I
9. .... F I
10. .... F I
11. .... F I
12. .... F I

C. *Listen to the following questions; some begin with* chi *and some with* che. *Repeat the question after the speaker and circle* chi *if the sentence starts with* chi, *or* che *if it starts with* che. *You will hear each sentence twice.*

1. .... chi che
2. .... chi che
3. .... chi che
4. .... chi che
5. .... chi che
6. .... chi che
7. .... chi che
8. .... chi che

D. *Listen to the following statements and tell whether they are affirmative or negative. During the pause, circle A if affirmative, N if negative. You will hear each sentence twice.*

1.	A	N	5.	A	N
2.	A	N	6.	A	N
3.	A	N	7.	A	N
4.	A	N			

E. *Listen to the following statements using forms of* avere. *Then circle the subject of each statement during the pause. You will hear each sentence twice.*

1.	io	tu	lei/lui	noi	voi	loro
2.	io	tu	lei/lui	noi	voi	loro
3.	io	tu	lei/lui	noi	voi	loro
4.	io	tu	lei/lui	noi	voi	loro
5.	io	tu	lei/lui	noi	voi	loro
6.	io	tu	lei/lui	noi	voi	loro

PRONUNCIATION

A. *Practice diphthongs with the two Italian semi-vowels /w/ and /j/. Repeat each word during the pause.*

/wɔ/ uomo, fuochi, fuori, ruota, uova, può, suola, duoli, vuoti, tuoni, scuola, buoni

/wa/ fatua, manuali, ingenua, mutua, Pasqua, quadro, quasi, quanto

/ja/ piani, fiati, liana, viali, Amalia, fiaschi, pianti, amianti

/ju/ piú, chiusi, abiura, piuma, fiumi, chiudi, liuti

B. *Now practice the same sounds in phrases. Repeat each of these phrases after the speaker.*

/w / un uomo è fuori   nuota e nuota   non ne può piú

/wa/ fatua e ingenua   ha quasi quarant'anni

NAME ______________________________ DATE ____________ CLASS ____________

/ja/ Amalia va piano   non fiata   nel viale di liane

/ju/ chiusi piume   aiuta   un liuto piú scuro

C. *The vowel sounds /e/ and /o/ do not exist in English in isolation. Listen to the following words carefully and repeat each during the pause. Try to reproduce them correctly.*

/e/ me, e, se, sete, te, pene, le, vede, alte, meni, deve, mele

/o/ o, sono, loro, giorno, sino, signore, come, mosto, lo, voto, solo

D. *Now practice these sounds in phrases. Repeat each word or phrase after the speaker.*

/e/ vendete   tele di seta cinese   nel mese della sete

/o/ Voto come loro   solo nel giorno   ci sono molti signori

D I C T A T I O N

Listen to the following sentences. Then write each sentence during the pause. Each sentence will be repeated so that you can check your accuracy.

1. ____

____

2. ____

____

3. ____

____

4. ____

____

5. ____

____

NAME ______________________ DATE __________ CLASS __________

D I A L O G U E

Listen to the following dialogue.

Signora Rossi: Dove abiti ora, Laura?
Laura: A piazza Garibaldi, e Lei?
Signora Rossi: Io abito a piazza Vivaldi numero dieci.
Laura: Abita in un palazzo moderno?
Signora Rossi: No, il palazzo non è molto moderno ma c'è l'ascensore.
Laura: Quanti piani ci sono?
Signora Rossi: Ci sono sei piani, e nel palazzo dove abiti tu?
Laura: Ci sono cinque piani e dieci appartamenti, e sul tetto c'è una bella terrazza.

Now repeat each sentence after the speaker.

G R A M M A T I C A

I. USE OF PREPOSITIONS

A. *Create new sentences by substituting in the base sentence the words given. Make contractions where needed.*

1. Example: Laura è ospite del padrone di casa
la zia
Laura è ospite della zia.

....

....

2. Example: La signora Spina telefona allo zio.
il medico
La signora Spina telefona al medico.

....

....

3. Example: Gli amici dello studente sono in Italia.
il padrone di casa
Gli amici del padrone di casa sono in Italia.

....

....

4. Example: Il programma è per il pianista.
gli americani
Il programma è per gli americani.

....

....

5. Example: Laura è con le amiche in un bar.
lo studente
Laura è con lo studente in un bar.

....

....

B. *Complete the following sentences using the preposition* su *plus the words given. Make the necessary contractions. Then repeat the correct sentence after the speaker gives it.*

Example: Gli ospiti sono (la terrazza)
Gli ospiti sono sulla terrazza.

1. .... 4. ....

2. .... 5. ....

3. ....

NAME ________________________________ DATE ____________ CLASS _____________

C. *Complete the following sentences using the preposition* in *plus the words given. Make the necessary contractions. Then repeat the correct sentence after the speaker gives it.*

Example: Ci sono cinque piani
il palazzo
Ci sono cinque piani nel palazzo.

1. .... 3. .... 5. ....

2. .... 4. ....

D. *Complete the following sentences with either* a *or* in *plus the place names given. Then repeat the correct sentence after the speaker gives it.*

Example: Firenze sta
Italia
Firenze sta in Italia.

1. .... 3. .... 5. ....

2. .... 4. .... 6. ....

II. PRESENT TENSE OF FIRST CONJUGATION VERBS ENDING IN -ARE

A. *Create new sentences by substituting in the base sentence the words given.*

1. Example: Il signor Fini abita a Roma.
gli inquilini
Gli inquilini abitano a Roma.

....

....

2. Example: Lo zio scherza con i giovani.
il medico
Il medico scherza con i giovani.

....

....

3. Example: Lo psichiatra esagera sempre.
le zie
Le zie esagerano sempre.

....

....

NAME ________________ DATE __________ CLASS __________

UNIT 3

Part Two

GRAMMATICA

PRESENT TENSE OF FIRST CONJUGATION VERBS, CONTINUED

Create new sentences by substituting in the base sentence the correct form of the verbs given.

1. Example: Tu giochi, io non gioco.
   parlare
   Tu parli, io non parlo.

   ....

   ....

2. Example: Voi giocate, noi non giochiamo.
   parlare
   Voi parlate, noi non parliamo.

   ....

   ....

3. Example: Loro giocano, lei non gioca.
   parlare
   Loro parlano, lei non parla.

   ....

   ....

NAME ______________________ DATE __________ CLASS __________

LISTENING/COMPREHENSION

Listen to the following dialogue.

GLI INQUILINI DI PIAZZA GARIBALDI

Mentre passeggiano sul Lungotevere, Laura parla con il suo amico Giacomo degli inquilini del palazzo dove abita.

Giacomo: Dove abiti ora, Laura?
Laura: A piazza Garibaldi numero tre.
Giacomo: Quanti piani ci sono nel palazzo?
Laura: Ci sono cinque piani e dieci appartamenti. Non è una palazzina molto moderna ma c'è l'ascensore e una bella terrazza sul tetto.
Giacomo: Scommetto che sei amica di tutti gli inquilini del palazzo. Parli con tutti, vero?
Laura: No, non parlo con tutti. Vediamo: saluto sempre il padrone di casa, il signor Rossi, e la signora del primo piano.
Giacomo: Chi abita al primo piano?
Laura: La signora Spina.
Giacomo: Vive sola?
Laura: No, vive con il marito. Dice che vive lí dal 1900.
Giacomo: Non è possibile. Quanti anni ha?
Laura: Non so, forse cento.
Giacomo: Tu scherzi sempre.

QUESTIONS

You will hear six statements about the passage you have just heard. Circle Sí *if the statement is true and* No *if the statement is false. You will hear each statement twice.*

1. .... Sí No
2. .... Sí No
3. .... Sí No
4. .... Sí No
5. .... Sí No
6. .... Sí No

INTONATION AND SOUND DISCRIMINATION

A. *Change the following statements into questions by changing the intonation.*

1. ....
2. ....
3. ....
4. ....
5. ....

NAME ______________________________ DATE ___________ CLASS ____________

B. *You will hear contractions of prepositions with the definite article. Tell which preposition has been contracted by circling it during the pause. You will hear each sentence twice.*

1\. .... a di da in su

2\. .... a di da in su

3\. .... a di da in su

4\. .... a di da in su

5\. .... a di da in su

6\. .... a di da in su

7\. .... a di da in su

8\. .... a di da in su

9\. .... a di da in su

C. *These sentences contain forms of verbs ending in* -are. *Circle the subject of each sentence during the pause. You will hear each sentence twice.*

1\. .... io tu lei/lui noi voi loro

2\. .... io tu lei/lui noi voi loro

3\. .... io tu lei/lui noi voi loro

4\. .... io tu lei/lui noi voi loro

5\. .... io tu lei/lui noi voi loro

6\. .... io tu lei/lui noi voi loro

NUMBERS

A. *Read the following numbers after the speaker. Look at the corresponding figures in your lab manual as you read. You will be building a large number from its component parts. Repeat the large number after the speaker gives it.*

due mila . . . due cento . . . venti . . . due
duemiladuecentoventidue

tremila . . . trecento . . . trenta . . . tre
tremilatrecentotrentatré

quattromila . . . quattrocento . . . quaranta . . . quattro
quattromilaquattrocentoquarantaquattro

cinquemila . . . cinquecento . . . cinquanta . . . cinque
cinquemilacinquecentocinquantacinque

seimila . . . seicento . . . sessanta . . . sei
seimilaseicentosessantasei

settemila . . . settecento . . . settanta . . . sette
settemilasettecentosettantasette

ottomila . . . ottocento . . . ottanta . . . otto
ottomilaottocentottantotto

novemila . . . novecento . . . novanta . . . nove
novemilanovecentonovantanove

B. *Listen to the following Italian numbers. Repeat them after the speaker, then circle the number you hear in your manual. You will hear each number twice.*

1. .... 6 7 8

2. .... 7 8 9

3. .... 12 13 14

4. .... 15 16 17

5. .... 17 18 19

6. .... 26 36 46

7. .... 53 63 73

8. .... 260 270 370

9. .... 582 492 592

C. *Repeat the following arithmetic problems after the speaker. Repeat each again after the speaker. As you speak, follow the figures written in your manual.*

1. 3 - 1 = 2

2. 4 + 3 = 7

3. 16 - 14 = 2

4. 19 + 20 = 39

NAME ______________________ DATE __________ CLASS __________

P R O N U N C I A T I O N

THE SOUNDS /e/ /ɛ/ CONTRASTED

A. *Repeat after the speaker the following pairs of words in which the sounds /e/ and /ɛ/ are contrasted. Try to make the contrast clear and accurate. The acute accent (´) indictes /e/; the grave account (`) indicates /ɛ/. A dot under a vowel indicates where the stress falls.*

/e/ /ɛ/ é-è . . . pésca-pèsca . . . mézzo-mèzzo . . . péste-pèste . . .

accétta-accètta . . . désti-dèsti . . .. séte-sètte . . .

néttare-nèttare . . . sé-sèi . . . séppe-sèrpe . . .

affétto-affètto

THE SOUNDS /o/ /ɔ/ CONTRASTED

B. *Repeat the following words in which the sounds /o/ and /ɔ/ are contrasted. Try to make the contrast accurate. The acute accent (´) indicates (o); the grave accent (`) indicates /ɔ/.*

/o/ /ɔ/ ó-hò . . . córso-còrso . . . dótto-dòtto . . . póse-pòse . . .

pórtó-pòrtó . . . fórato-fòra . . . fósse-fòsse . . .

mótóre-mòtó . . . lóró-l'òró . . . vóltó-vòltó . . .

vólgó-vòlgó

C. *You will hear eight words in which either the sound /e/ or /ɛ/ occurs. Circle* uno *if the sound in the word is /e/, and* due *if the sound is /ɛ/. You will hear each word twice.*

....	uno	due	....	uno	due
....	uno	due	....	uno	due
....	uno	due	....	uno	due
....	uno	due	....	uno	due

D. *You will hear eight words in which either the sound /o/ or /ɔ/ occurs. Circle* uno *if the sound in the word is /o/, and* due *if the sound is /ɔ/. You will hear each word twice.*

....	uno	due	....	uno	due
....	uno	due	....	uno	due
....	uno	due	....	uno	due
....	uno	due	....	uno	due

D I C T A T I O N

Listen to the following sentences. Then write each sentence during the pause. Each sentence will be repeated so that you can check your accuracy.

1. ______________________________

   ____

2. ______________________________

   ____

3. ______________________________

   ____

4. ______________________________

   ____

5. ______________________________

   ____

NAME ______________________ DATE ____________ CLASS ____________

UNIT 4

Part One

D I A L O G U E

Listen to the following dialogue.

Maria: Di dove sei?
Angela: Sono di Londra.
Maria: Non sei italiana? Parli bene l'italiano.
Angela: No, non sono italiana, sono americana, ma vivo in Italia da molti anni. E tu di dove sei?
Maria: Io sono italiana, di Roma.
Angela: Parli inglese?
Maria: Sí, parlo inglese e francese ma non li parlo bene.

Now repeat each sentence after the speaker.

G R A M M A T I C A

I. PRESENT TENSE OF SECOND CONJUGATION VERBS ENDING IN *-ERE*

A. *Create new sentences by substituting in the base sentence the words given.*

1. Example: Gli studenti leggono il telegramma.
   Laura
   Laura legge il telegramma.

   ....

   ....

2. Example: Gli inquilini prendono l'ascensore.
   Il padrone di casa
   Il padrone di casa prende l'ascensore.

   ....

   ....

3. Example: La studentessa perde il gettone del telefono.
gli americani
Gli americani perdono il gettone del telefono.

....

....

B. *Create new sentences by substituting in the base sentences the correct forms of the words given.*

1. Example: Vendi il programma, tu? No, non vendo il programma.
leggere
Leggi il programma, tu? No, non leggo il programma.

....

....

2. Example: Mettete il gettone? No, non mettiamo il gettone.
perdere
Perdete il gettone? No, non perdiamo il gettone.

....

....

II. IDIOMATIC USES OF *AVERE*

A. *Create new sentences by substituting in the base sentence the words given.*

1. Example: Laura ha fretta.
i medici
I medici hanno fretta.

....

....

2. Example: Il medico ha sempre ragione.
noi
Abbiamo sempre ragione.

....

....

NAME ______________________ DATE __________ CLASS __________

3. Example: Gli americani hanno caldo in Italia.
lo straniero
Lo straniero ha caldo in Italia.

....

....

B. *Answer the following questions in the negative. Then repeat the correct sentence after the speaker gives it.*

Example: Hai fame stasera?
No, non ho fame stasera.

1. .... 2. .... 3. ....

C. *Answer the following questions as in the example. Then repeat the correct sentence after the speaker gives it.*

Example: Quanti anni ha Giacomo?
Giacomo ha diciotto anni.

1. .... 2. .... 3. ....

III. USES OF *C'È, CI SONO, ECCO*

A. *Change the following sentences from singular to plural. Then repeat the correct sentence after the speaker gives it.*

1. Example: Ecco la casa sulla piazza.
Ecco le case sulla piazza.

....

....

2. Example: C'è lo zio a casa.
Ci sono gli zii a casa.

....

....

B. *Change the following sentences from plural to singular. Then repeat the correct sentence after the speaker gives it.*

Example: Ecco i palazzi di piazza Garibaldi.
Ecco il palazzo di piazza Garibaldi.

....

....

NAME ______________________ DATE __________ CLASS __________

UNIT 4

Part Two

G R A M M A T I C A

VERB REVIEW

Create new sentences by substituting in the following base sentences the subjects supplied.

Example: La studentessa parla al telefono.

io:	*Parlo al telefono.*	*noi:*	*Parliamo al telefono.*
tu:	*Parli al telefono.*	*voi:*	*Parlate al telefono.*
lui:	*Parla al telefono.*	*loro:*	*Parlano al telefono.*

1. Example: Laura vive a Roma.

....

....

2. Example: L'amica è di Chicago.

....

....

3. Example: Lo zio abita a New York negli Stati Uniti.

....

....

4. Example: L'ospite ha fame.

....

....

L I S T E N I N G / C O M P R E H E N S I O N

Listen to the following dialogue.

DAL MEDICO

Bruce e Joy Bryant, gli amici di Giacomo, arrivano dal medico. Parlano con l'infermiera.

Joy: Abbiamo un appuntamento con la dottoressa.
Infermiera: A che ora?
Joy: Alle dieci.
Infermiera: Loro sono i signori Bryant?
Joy: Sí, siamo Joy e Bruce Bryant.
Infermiera: Non sono italiani, vero?
Joy: No.
Infermiera: Di dove sono?
Joy: Io sono americana, di Chicago, e mio marito è inglese, di Londra.
Infermiera: Parlano bene l'italiano. Vivono qui in Italia?
Joy: No, viviamo negli Stati Uniti. Siamo a Roma da due giorni, ospiti della famiglia Fini.
Infermiera: Dove stanno a Roma?
Joy: Abitiamo in via dell'Arte 6, interno 4.
Infermiera: Quanti anni hanno?
Bruce: Mia moglie ha venti anni e io ventidue.
Infermiera: Come si sentono?
Bruce: Per niente bene.
Infermiera: Che cosa hanno?
Bruce: Abbiamo mal di testa, mal di stomaco, la nausea e la febbre.
Infermiera: Questo non è raffreddore. Per me è l'influenza. Ma ecco la dottoressa.

QUESTIONS

You will hear eight statements about the passage you have just heard. Circle Sí *if the statement is true, and* No *if the statement is false. You will hear each statement twice.*

1. .... Sí No 5. .... Sí No

2. .... Sí No 6. .... Sí No

3. .... Sí No 7. .... Sí No

4. .... Sí No 8. .... Sí No

NAME ______________________ DATE __________ CLASS __________

I N T O N A T I O N   A N D
S O U N D   D I S C R I M I N A T I O N

A. *You will hear short sentences using forms of verbs ending in* -ere. *Circle the subject of the verb during the pause. You will hear each sentence twice.*

1. .... io tu lei/lui noi voi loro
2. .... io tu lei/lui noi voi loro
3. .... io tu lei/lui noi voi loro
4. .... io tu lei/lui noi voi loro
5. .... io tu lei/lui noi voi loro
6. .... io tu lei/lui noi voi loro

B. *Tell whether the following sentences are singular or plural. Circle* S *if singular,* P *if plural. You will hear each sentence twice.*

1. .... S P
2. .... S P
3. .... S P
4. .... S P
5. .... S P
6. .... S P
7. .... S P
8. .... S P

C. *Tell whether the subjects of the following sentences are singular or plural and masculine or feminine by circling* S *if singular,* P *if plural and also* M *if masculine,* F *if feminine. You will hear each sentence twice.*

1. .... S P M F
2. .... S P M F
3. .... S P M F
4. .... S P M F
5. .... S P M F
6. .... S P M F
7. .... S P M F

N U M B E R S

A. *Listen to the following numbers. Repeat them after the speaker and circle the corresponding figure at right. You will hear each number twice.*

1.	10	11	12
2.	17	18	19
3.	46	47	56
4.	66	67	77
5.	361	371	471
6.	496	497	596

B. *Repeat the following arithmetic problems after the speaker. Repeat them again after the speaker. Follow the corresponding figures written in your lab manual.*

1. 54 - 21 = 33
2. 87 - 42 = 45
3. 756 + 143 = 899
4. 534 + 241 = 775

P R O N U N C I A T I O N

THE SOUNDS /e/ /ɛ/

Practice the sounds /e/ and /ɛ/ in sentences. Repeat each sentence after the speaker. Concentrate on correct pronunciation.

/e/ /ɛ/ La névé è bèlla
èra la notté néra
métti tré mélé intèré
nélla césta di Vèra
sènté vénti vènti
sé né viéné
lèsta é mèsta
la mèssé fu méssa via
ha sété allé sètté
pésca lé pèsché
tra lé péré
la pèsté métté
la gènté néllé pésté

NAME ______________________ DATE __________ CLASS __________

THE SOUNDS /o/ /ɔ/

Practice the sounds /o/ and /ɔ/ in phrases. Repeat each phrase after the speaker. Concentrate on pronouncing correctly.

/o/ /ɔ/

óttọne	pọ̀rtó il lọ́ró
il cọ́rsó	óróḷọ̀gió d'ọ̀ró
ha cọ́rsó mọ́ltó	sọ́ttó il pọ́nte
sọ́nó sọ́ló	la cọ́rrente è fọ̀rte
e hò sọ̀nnó	pọ̀rtó mọ́ntóni al fọ́nte
ne hò ọ̀ttó ó nọ̀ve	cọ́rta fu la sọ̀rte del cọ́nte
sónó rọ̀se	cọ́rse, cọ́rse pọ̀i ló cọ̀lse
rọ́sse ó rọ̀sa?	

THE SOUNDS /o/, /i/, /e/, /a/ and /u/ IN UNSTRESSED SYLLABLES

Listen carefully to the following words in which the stress falls on the third syllable from the end. Remember that in Italian short or unstressed vowels keep the same sound as long or stressed vowels. Repeat each word after the speaker.

/o/ tavolo . . . avolo . . . Tivoli . . . anemone

/i/ asino . . . idillico . . . serica . . . mettila

/e/ angelo . . . ponetela . . . annovera . . . idrogeno

/a/ amano . . . tipografo . . . cantano . . . megalomane

/u/ rotula . . . incolume . . . colubre . . . incuba

D I C T A T I O N

Listen to the following sentences. Then write each sentence during the pause. Each sentence will be repeated so that you can check your accuracy.

1. ______________________________

____

2. ______________________________

____

3. ____

____

4. ____

____

5. ____

____

NAME ______________________ DATE __________ CLASS __________

UNIT 5

Part One

D I A L O G U E

Listen to the following dialogue.

Salumiere: Buon giorno, signorina. Che cosa desidera oggi?
Laura: Vorrei del formaggio.
Salumiere: Di che tipo?
Laura: Quel formaggio bianco e verde, che tipo è?
Salumiere: Quello è gorgonzola. È un formaggio molto forte e saporito.
Laura: Bene, me ne dia un etto.
Salumiere: Vuole altro?
Laura: No grazie, quanto Le devo?
Salumiere: 800 lire in tutto. Paghi alla cassa per favore.

Now repeat each sentence after the speaker.

G R A M M A T I C A

I. THE INDEFINITE ARTICLE

A. *Create new sentences by substituting in the base sentence the words given.*

1. Example: Ecco una casa.
   studente
   Ecco uno studente.

   ....

   ....

2. Example: Non è un salumiere.
   studente
   Non è uno studente.

   ....

   ....

B. *Answer the following questions as in the example. Then repeat the correct answer after the speaker gives it.*

Example: C'è un palazzo qui?
Ecco il palazzo.

1. .... 3. .... 5. ....

2. .... 4. ....

C. *You will hear the same five questions and answers again. Change both question and answer from singular to plural. Repeat the correct sentences after the speaker gives them.*

Example: C'è un palazzo qui? Ecco il palazzo!
Ci sono dei palazzi qui? Ecco i palazzi!

1. .... 3. .... 5. ....

2. .... 4. ....

II. ADJECTIVES

A. *Create new sentences by substituting in the base sentence the words given.*

Example: Ecco un formaggio fresco.
formaggi
Ecco dei formaggi freschi.

....

....

B. *Change the following sentences from singular to plural. Then repeat the correct sentence after the speaker gives it.*

Example: Il salame è saporito.
I salami sono saporiti.

....

....

Example: Il tavolo non è nero, è verde.
I tavoli non sono neri, sono verdi.

1. .... 3. .... 5. ....

2. .... 4. ....

NAME ______________________ DATE ____________ CLASS ____________

III. DEMONSTRATIVES: *QUESTO, QUELLO*

A. *Create new sentences by sbustituting in the base sentence the nouns given.*

1. Example: Voglio questo pane non quello.
   sfilatini
   Voglio questi sfilatini non quelli.

   ....

   ....

2. Example: Desidera quel formaggio o questo?
   scatola
   Desidera quella scatola o questa?

   ....

   ....

3. Example: Compro queste case non quelle.
   casa
   Compro questa casa non quella.

   ....

   ....

IV. COMPARISON OF ADJECTIVES WITH *MENO* AND *PIÙ*

A. *Change the following sentences by adding* più di + *the noun given, as in the example. Repeat the correct sentence after the speaker gives it.*

Example: La casa è bassa.
il palazzo
La casa è più bassa del palazzo.

1. ....
2. ....
3. ....
4. ....
5. ....

B. *Change the following sentences by adding* meno di + *the noun given, as in the example. Repeat the correct sentence after the speaker gives it.*

Example: La casa è bianca.
il palazzo
La casa è meno bianca del palazzo.

....

....

NAME ____________________ DATE ____________ CLASS ____________

UNIT 5

Part Two

GRAMMATICA

PRESENT OF MODAL VERBS: *POTERE, VOLERE, DOVERE*

A. *Create new sentences by substituting in the base sentence the modal verbs given.*

Example: Non puoi dirlo in metri?
volete
Non volete dirlo in metri?

....

....

B. *Create new sentences by substituting in the base sentence the subjects given.*

1. Example: La signora deve pagare alla cassa.
gli inquilini
Gli inquilini devono pagare alla cassa.

....

....

2. Example: L'ospite può telefonare al padrone di casa.
gli ospiti
Gli ospiti possono telefonare al padrone di casa.

....

....

3. Example: Giacomo vuole stare a casa.
tu
Vuoi stare a casa.

....

....

L I S T E N I N G / C O M P R E H E N S I O N

Listen to the following dialogue.

IL SISTEMA METRICO

Giacomo e Laura parlano di pesi e misure.

Laura: Non capisco perché molte persone non vogliono dire la loro età.
Giacomo: Chissà. Tu quando sei nata?
Laura: Nel millenovecentosessanta, e tu quando sei nato?
Giacomo: Siamo nati nello stesso anno. Quanto sei alta?
Laura: Cinque piedi e sei pollici.
Giacomo: Queste misure americane mi confondono. Non puoi dirlo in metri o in centimetri?
Laura: Vediamo...un pollice misura circa 2.50 centimetri.
Giacomo: Un piede misura circa 30 centimetri e 6 pollici.
Laura: Allora sono alta 1,65 metri.
Giacomo: Vuoi sapere quanto sono alto io?
Laura: Certamente.
Giacomo: Un metro e ottanta.
Laura: Allora sei 15 centimetri più alto di me. E quanto pesi?
Giacomo: Settantacinque chili.
Laura: Voglio il peso in libbre.
Giacomo: Una libbra è più o meno mezzo chilo. Allora peso circa 165 libbre. Tu quanto pesi?
Laura: Indovina! Posso solo dirti che peso meno di te.
Giacomo: Vediamo...pesi meno di me, non sei più magra di me, non sei più grassa di me ma sei più bassa...pesi 115 libbre.
Laura: Hai sbagliato. Peso 110 libbre o 50 chili.

QUESTIONS

You will hear six questions about the dialogue you have just heard. Indicate the correct answer to each question by circling the letter before it. You will hear each question twice.

1. ....

a. nel millenovecentosessantacinque

b. nel millenovecentosessanta

c. nel millenovecentosessantuno

NAME ______________________ DATE __________ CLASS __________

2. ....

a. è piú alta di Giacomo

b. cinque piedi e cinque pollici

c. un metro e sessantacinque

3. ....

a. circa un metro

b. circa trenta centimetri

c. circa due centimetri e mezzo

4. ....

a. cinque chili

b. una libbra

c. mezzo chilo

5. ....

a. perché è piú bassa

b. perché è piú grassa

c. perché è piú alta

6. ....

a. quindici libbre

b. ottanta libbre

c. centodieci libbre

INTONATION AND SOUND DISCRIMINATION

A. *Change the following statements into questions by changing the intonation. Repeat each question after the speaker.*

Example: Pesi cinquanta chili.
Pesi cinquanta chili?

1. ....
2. ....
3. ....
4. ....
5. ....

B. *Tell whether the following sentences are singular or plural by circling* S *or* P. *You will hear each sentence twice.*

.... S P .... S P

.... S P .... S P

.... S P .... S P

C. *Listen to the following short sentences, which contain forms of either* volere *or* potere. *During the pause, circle either* volere *or* potere *and the subject of the verb. You will hear each sentence twice.*

1. .... volere potere io tu lei/lui noi voi loro

2. .... volere potere io tu lei/lui noi voi loro

3. .... volere potere io tu lei/lui noi voi loro

4. .... volere potere io tu lei/lui noi voi loro

5. .... volere potere io tu lei/lui noi voi loro

6. .... volere potere io tu lei/lui noi voi loro

D. *Listen to the following questions and tell whether they are asked in formal or informal address. During the pause, circle* F *for formal or* I *for informal. You will hear each sentence twice.*

1.	F	I	5.	F	I
2.	F	I	6.	F	I
3.	F	I	7.	F	I
4.	F	I	8.	F	I

P R O N U N C I A T I O N

THE SOUNDS /l̃/ and /ñ/

A. *The sound /l̃/ does not exist in English. In order to reproduce it, you have to pronounce two sounds at the same time: /l/ and /j/. Put a lot of energy into doing so. Notice that this is a wet sound and you have to feel your mouth moist when you pronounce it. Repeat each word after the speaker:*

figlio . . . foglio . . . maglia . . . aglio . . . daglielo . . . glielo . . . gli

Contrast these pairs and repeat:

olio/figlio . . . Amalia/maglia . . . lieto/glielo

NAME ______________ DATE ________ CLASS ________

B. *Now practice the sound /l̃/ in phrases. Repeat each phrase.*

Amalia e Delia   le figlie di Giulio   daglieli con aglio e olio

vogliono un milione   per pigliare   quelle biglie ammaliate

C. *Another sound that does not exist in English is /ñ/. This sound, too, is the mixture of two sounds: /n/ and /j/. When you pronounce this sound, feel your tongue squeezed between the upper and lower teeth with considerable energy. Repeat each word after the speaker:*

gnocco   gnu   legnate   agogno   lignite

indegne   magnate

Contrast these pairs and repeat:

Antonio/agogno   veniate/legnate   paniere/magnete

D. *Now practice the sound /ñ/ in phrases. Repeat each phrase.*

la degna signora   annienta agnostici gnomi   agnelli nani

Antonia si lagna   le castagne non ci sono in giugno

segna la legna   non le pigne

D I C T A T I O N

Listen to the following sentences. Then write each sentence during the pause. Each sentence will be repeated so that you can check your accuracy.

1. ______________________________

____

2. ______________________________

____

3. ______________________________

____

4. ______________________________

____

5. ______________________________

____

NAME ______________________ DATE ____________ CLASS ____________

UNIT 6

Part One

D I A L O G U E

Listen to the following dialogue.

NOTIZIE DALL'ITALIA

Laura e Gianna, un'amica italiana, parlano di giornali, di politica e di altre cose.

Gianna: Leggi i giornali italiani?
Laura: Sí, li leggo ma non capisco tutto.
Gianna: Che cosa non capisci?
Laura: La politica italiana, per esempio, io non la seguo. È troppo complicata.
Gianna: I giovani italiani leggono molti giornali e finiscono sempre per discutere di politica, ma non sempre capiscono tutto.

Now repeat each sentence after the speaker.

G R A M M A T I C A

I. PRESENT TENSE OF THIRD CONJUGATION VERBS ENDING IN -*IRE*

A. *Create new sentences by substituting in the base sentence the words given.*

1. Example: Laura parte domani mattina.
voi
Partite domani mattina.

....

....

2. Example: La zia dorme sempre.
gli studenti
Gli studenti dormono sempre.

....

....

3. Example: Gli studenti non capiscono la lezione.
io
Non capisco la lezione.

....

....

II. ADJECTIVES THAT PRECEDE THE NOUN: *BELLO, BUONO,* ETC.

A. *Change the following sentences from singular to plural. Then repeat the correct sentence after the speaker gives it.*

Example: Ecco una buona notizia.
Ecco delle buone notizie.

1. .... 3. .... 5. ....

2. .... 4. .... 6. ....

B. *Change the following sentences by adding the adjectives given, placing them either before or after the noun as required. Then repeat the correct sentence after the speaker gives it.*

Examples: 1. Ecco delle studentesse.
bravo
Ecco delle brave studentesse.

2. Ecco un palazzo.
moderno
Ecco un palazzo moderno.

1. .... 3. .... 5. ....

2. .... 4. .... 6. ....

NAME ______________________ DATE __________ CLASS ____________

III. QUANTIFIERS: *MOLTO, TROPPO, POCO*

A. *Create new sentences by substituting in the base sentence the words given.*

1. Example: Il salumiere non vende molto olio.
   olive
   Il salumiere non vende molte olive.

   ....

   ....

2. Example: Voglio comprare poca pasta.
   sfilatini
   Voglio comprare pochi sfilatini.

   ....

   ....

3. Example: Qui ci sono troppe macchine.
   giornali
   Qui ci sono troppi giornali.

   ....

   ....

IV. PRESENT TENSE OF SOME IRREGULAR VERBS: *DIRE, DARE, ANDARE, SAPERE*

A. *Create new sentences by substituting in the base sentence the subjects given.*

1. Example: Gli ospiti stranieri dicono che l'Italia è bella.
   Giacomo
   Giacomo dice che l'Italia è bella.

   ....

   ....

2. Example: Io non so niente.
   gli ospiti
   Gli ospiti non sanno niente.

   ....

   ....

3. Example: I giornali danno delle buone notizie.
il giornale
Il giornale dà delle buone notizie.

....

....

4. Example: Gli studenti vanno a Roma domani.
tu
Tu vai a Roma domani.

....

....

V. USE OF THE PARTITIVE

A. *Change the following sentences from positive to negative. Then repeat the correct sentence after the speaker gives it.*

Example: Voglio del pane.
Non voglio pane.

1. .... 3. .... 5. ....

2. .... 4. .... 6. ....

B. *Answer the following questions using the partitive. Then repeat the correct sentence after the speaker gives it.*

Example: Vuole il caffè per la zia?
Sì, preferisco del caffè per la zia.

1. .... 3. .... 5. ....

2. .... 4. ....

NAME ______________________ DATE __________ CLASS __________

UNIT 6

Part Two

G R A M M A T I C A

VERB REVIEW

A. *Create new sentences by substituting in the base sentence the subjects given.*

1. Example: I giovani leggono i giornali e danno molte notizie.
   il medico
   Il medico legge i giornali e dà molte notizie.

   ....

   ....

2. Example: Quando parte per Firenze, va in macchina.
   Giacomo
   Quando Giacomo parte per Firenze, va in macchina.

   ....

   ....

3. Example: Le gente agisce con buon senso se vuole.
   noi
   Agiamo con buon senso se vogliamo.

   ....

   ....

4. Example: Se possono gli ospiti vanno sempre a piedi.
   io
   Se posso vado sempre a piedi.

   ....

   ....

L I S T E N I N G / C O M P R E H E N S I O N

Listen to the following dialogue.

UNA VISITA A LAURA

Joy e la signora Fini decidono di andare a trovare Laura.

Signora Fini:	Andiamo a casa di Laura?
Joy:	Volentieri. Come ci andiamo?
Signora Fini:	Io di solito ci vado a piedi. Non è lontana. Se vuoi, però, andiamo in macchina.
Joy:	Quanto è lontana?
Signora Fini:	Non so, ma è vicina...al massimo mezzo chilometro.
Joy:	No, no. Andiamo a piedi se preferisce.
Signora Fini:	Sí, faccio volentieri due passi.

(Piú tardi a casa di Laura)

Laura:	Posso offrirvi il caffè?
Signora Fini:	Io prendo volentieri il tè.
Joy:	Per me una tazza di caffè va benissimo.
Laura:	Lei, signora, vuole il latte o il limone nel tè?
Signora Fini:	Il latte, grazie, e lo zucchero.
Laura:	Ecco dei biscotti e della torta.
Joy:	Grazie.
Laura:	*(a Joy)* Quando parte Bruce per Firenze?
Joy:	Bruce non parte solo; partiamo insieme.
Laura:	Ah sí, quando partite?
Joy:	Domani mattina.
Laura:	A che ora?
Joy:	Non so ancora. Quando vado alla stazione a comprare i biglietti, controllo l'orario dei treni.
Signora Fini:	Ti diamo noi un orario; l'abbiamo a casa.
Joy:	Grazie mille!

QUESTIONS

You will hear nine statements about the dialogue you have just heard. Circle Sí *if the statement is true, and* No *if the statement is false. You will hear each statement twice.*

1.	Sí	No	6.	Sí	No
2.	Sí	No	7.	Sí	No
3.	Sí	No	8.	Sí	No
4.	Sí	No	9.	Sí	No
5.	Sí	No			

NAME ______________________ DATE __________ CLASS __________

INTONATION AND SOUND DISCRIMINATION

A. *Practice the following progressive variations. Repeat after each pause.*

1. andate in macchina?
   andate sempre in macchina?
   voi andate sempre in macchina, a casa?
   voi andate sempre in macchina, a casa di Pino?
2. quando parte?
   quando parte il suo amico?
   quando parte il suo amico per Firenze?

B. *The following short sentences contain forms of either* dire *or* dare. *During the pause, circle either* dire *or* dare *and the subject of the verb that you hear. You will hear each sentence twice.*

1.	....	dire	dare	io	tu	lei/lui	noi	voi	loro
2.	....	dire	dare	io	tu	lei/lui	noi	voi	loro
3.	....	dire	dare	io	tu	lei/lui	noi	voi	loro
4.	....	dire	dare	io	tu	lei/lui	noi	voi	loro
5.	....	dire	dare	io	tu	lei/lui	noi	voi	loro
6.	....	dire	dare	io	tu	lei/lui	noi	voi	loro
7.	....	dire	dare	io	tu	lei/lui	noi	voi	loro
8.	....	dire	dare	io	tu	lei/lui	noi	voi	loro

THE TIME

Change the time in the following sentences from the twenty-four-hour clock to the twelve-hour clock. Then repeat the correct sentence after the speaker gives it.

Example: Sono andato alla stazione alle quattordici.
Sono andato alla stazione alle due.

1. .... 3. .... 5. ....

2. .... 4. .... 6. ....

P R O N U N C I A T I O N

THE CONSONANT /r/

In order to make this very Italian sound, place your tongue against your upper teeth and allow the tip to vibrate freely while letting your voice sound. Keep your throat relaxed.

Repeat: Roma . . . rosa . . . caro . . . Mario . . . Teresa . . . farò . . . tara

Like all Italian consonants, the /r/ sound can be uttered with high energy or low energy. It is very important to distinguish these two sounds because the meaning of a word may change depending on which sound is used. In spelling, the high energy consonant sounds are marked by doubling of the consonant. All vowels before a high energy consonant sound become very short, whereas they are long before a low energy sound. But remember that short vowels are pronounced as distinctly as long vowels--only the length is reduced.

Practice contrasting high and low energy /r/ in these pairs of words.

Repeat: caro/carro . . . Mara/marra . . . poro/porro . . . sera/serra . . . mira/mirra . . . dura/durra

Practice these sounds in phrases:

caro amore . . . arde di febbre . . . il carro non parte . . .
la morte è forte . . . pone il porro nel poro

Write the following words. Each word will be repeated so that you can check your accuracy.

NAME ______________________ DATE ____________ CLASS ____________

D I C T A T I O N

Listen to the following sentences, then write each sentence during the pause. Each sentence will be repeated so that you can check your accuracy.

1. ____

____

2. ____

____

3. ____

____

4. ____

____

5. ____

____

NAME ______________________ DATE __________ CLASS __________

DIALOGUE

Listen to the following dialogue.

APPUNTAMENTO ALLE SETTE

Sono le cinque del pomeriggio. Laura telefona a casa Bianchi, a Firenze.

Laura: Pronto? C'è la signora Carla Bianchi, per favore?
Carla: Sono io. Chi parla?
Laura: Buon giorno, signora. Io sono Laura Ritter. Come stanno i Suoi amici?
Carla: Bene, grazie.
Laura: Il mio amico Giacomo Fini non ha potuto telefonarLe, così ha dato il Suo numero a me.
Carla: Ha fatto bene.

Now repeat each sentence during the pause.

GRAMMATICA

I. POSSESSIVES

A. *Change the following sentences by adding the possessives given. Then repeat the correct sentence after the speaker gives it.*

Example: Vado a Firenze con la macchina.
loro
Vado a Firenze con la loro macchina.

1. .... 3. .... 5. ....

2. .... 4. ....

Example: La casa non è grande.
tuo
La tua casa non è grande.

1. .... 3. .... 5. ....

2. .... 4. ....

B. *Change the following sentences from plural to singular. Then repeat the correct sentence after the speaker gives it.*

Example: Non sono i miei amici.
Non è il mio amico.

1. .... 3. .... 5. ....

2. .... 4. .... 6. ....

II. THE POSSESSIVE WITH KINSHIP TERMS

A. *Create new sentences by substituting in the base sentence the words given.*

1. Example: Anche suo marito è amico dei Bryant?
zia
Anche sua zia è amica dei Bryant?

....

....

2. Example: Anche tuo marito telefona domani?
nonna
Anche tua nonna telefona domani?

....

....

3. Example: Anche mio marito è a casa?
cognata
Anche mia cognata è a casa?

....

....

NAME ________________________ DATE ____________ CLASS ____________

B. *Change the following sentences from singular to plural. Then repeat the correct sentence after the speaker gives it.*

Example: Tuo zio prende il caffè.
I tuoi zii prendono il caffè.

1. .... 3. .... 5. ....

2. .... 4. .... 6. ....

III. THE COMPOUND PAST: *ESSERE* AND *AVERE* WITH THE PAST PARTICIPLE

A. *Create new sentences by substituting in the base sentence the words given.*

1. Example: Un tuo amico ha telefonato oggi.
gli zii
Gli zii hanno telefonato oggi.

....

....

2. Example: Hanno avuto un incidente.
gli ospiti
Gli ospiti hanno avuto un incidente.

....

....

3. Example: Gli ospiti sono partiti oggi pomeriggio.
Laura
Laura è partita oggi pomeriggio.

....

....

4. Example: I miei amici sono andati in treno.
un loro amico
Un loro amico è andato in treno.

....

....

B. *Change the following sentences from the present to the compound past, using either* essere *or* avere *as required. Then repeat the correct sentence after the speaker gives it.*

Example: Ha un incidente e non arriva a Firenze.
Ha avuto un incidente e non è arrivato a Firenze.

1. ....   3. ....

2. ....   4. ....

C. *Change the following sentences from the compound past to the present. Then repeat the correct sentence during the second pause.*

Example: La signora Fini è arrivata in macchina.
La signora Fini arriva in macchina.

1. ....   3. ....

2. ....   4. ....

NAME ______________________ DATE __________ CLASS __________

UNIT 7

Part Two

GRAMMATICA

THE COMPOUND PAST WITH MODAL VERBS

A. *Change the following sentences by adding the modal verb supplied. Then repeat the correct sentence after the speaker gives it.*

Example: La mia amica è andata in macchina
dovere
La mia amica è dovuta andare in macchina.

....

....

B. *Answer the following questions in the negative, and in the compound past, as in the examples. Then repeat the correct sentence after the speaker gives it.*

Examples: 1. La mia amica deve andare in macchina oggi?
No, la mia amica è dovuta andare in macchina ieri.

2. Gli ospiti devono comprare il biglietto oggi?
No, gli ospiti hanno dovuto comprare il biglietto ieri.

1. .... 3. .... 5. ....

2. .... 4. ....

L I S T E N I N G / C O M P R E H E N S I O N

Listen to the following dialogue.

UN INCIDENTE STRADALE

Giacomo incontra la sua amica Laura per la strada.

Giacomo: Hai sentito la brutta notizia?
Laura: No, non ho sentito niente.
Giacomo: Joy e Bruce hanno avuto un incidente di macchina.
Laura: Ma no, poveretti! Prima l'influenza e ora l'incidente. Come stanno?
Giacomo: Per fortuna non è niente di grave.
Laura: Ma non sono andati in treno?
Giacomo: No, all'ultimo momento hanno deciso di prendere la macchina.
Laura: Come l'hai saputo?
Giacomo: Un loro amico ha telefonato stamattina alle otto e ha raccontato tutto.
Laura: Ma sono mai arrivati a Firenze?
Giacomo: No, l'incidente è successo poco prima di Firenze.
Laura: Perché non andiamo a trovarli?
Giacomo: Ci ho pensato anch'io. Vuoi venire con me a Firenze? Parto oggi pomeriggio. Ho già comprato il biglietto.
Laura: Volentieri. Non sono mai stata a Firenze.
Giacomo: Fantastico!
Laura: A che ora parte il treno?
Giacomo: Se prendiamo quello delle quindici, cioè delle tre del pomeriggio, arriviamo stasera alle sei circa. È un treno veloce.
Laura: Bene. Allora ci vediamo alle due e mezzo alla stazione, o devo dire alle quattordici e trenta?

QUESTIONS

You will hear six questions about the dialogue you have just heard. Indicate the correct answer to each question by circling the letter before it. You will hear each question twice.

1. ....

a. Giacomo

b. Gli amici di Giacomo

c. Un amico di Firenze

2. ....

a. in treno

b. a piedi

c. in macchina

NAME ______________________ DATE ____________ CLASS ____________

3. ....

a. alla stazione

b. alle tre del pomeriggio

c. poco prima di Firenze

4. ....

a. a Firenze con la macchina

b. con il suo amico

c. alla stazione

5. ....

a. le diciannove

b. le tredici

c. le quindici

6. ....

a. con il treno delle tre

b. con il biglietto che ha comprato Giacomo

c. alle quattordici e trenta

INTONATION AND SOUND DISCRIMINATION

A. *Change the following questions into statements by changing the intonation.*

Example: Hai sentito la brutta notizia?
Hai sentito la brutta notizia.

1. .... 3. .... 5. ....

2. .... 4. .... 6. ....

B. *Listen to these short sentences in the compound past. Repeat each after the speaker, then circle either* avere *or* essere, *whichever is used, and circle the subject of the verb. You will hear each sentence twice.*

1.	avere	essere	io	tu	lei/lui	noi	voi	loro
2.	avere	essere	io	tu	lei/lui	noi	voi	loro
3.	avere	essere	io	tu	lei/lui	noi	voi	loro
4.	avere	essere	io	tu	lei/lui	noi	voi	loro
5.	avere	essere	io	tu	lei/lui	noi	voi	loro
6.	avere	essere	io	tu	lei/lui	noi	voi	loro
7.	avere	essere	io	tu	lei/lui	noi	voi	loro

C. *You will hear pairs of short sentences using possessives. Repeat each pair after the speaker. Pronounce carefully and notice how the possessive adjective agrees with its noun.*

1. Sono Maria. Ecco mio fratello e mia sorella.
2. Sono Gianni. Ecco la mia casa e il mio padrone di casa.
3. Sono Luisa. Ecco i miei ospiti e le mie amiche.
4. Siamo due sorelle. Ecco la nostra scuola e il nostro professore.
5. Siamo tre fratelli. Ecco il nostro treno ed i nostri biglietti.

PRONUNCIATION

SOUND AND SPELLING OF THE CONSONANT /k/

A. *The sound* /k/ *is pronounced as in English. However, like all consonant sounds in Italian, it may be uttered with either low energy or high energy. When* /k/ *is low energy, the preceding vowel is long; when it is high energy, the preceding vowel is short. Remember to pronounce short vowels just as distinctly as long vowels; only the length changes.*

Repeat these pairs after the speaker, contrasting high and low energy /k/.

seco/secco   oca/occhio   meco/mecca   fioco/fiocco

reca/ricca

B. *The sound* /k/ *has two possible spellings:* c *before* a, o, u, *or a consonant, and* ch *before* e *or* i. *If the sound is low energy, one* c *is written, while if it is high energy the* c *is doubled.*

Repeat each of these sentences after the speaker. Repeat each again after the speaker. Concentrate on pronouncing correctly.

peccato che sono lumache   compra fichi secchi   uno schiavo

cheto   s'inchinò accanto al cane

C. *Write the following words. They will be repeated so you can check your accuracy.*

NAME ______________________ DATE ____________ CLASS ____________

D. *If the sound* /k/ *is followed by the sounds* /wa/ /wo/ /we/, *the sequences are usually spelled* qua, quo, que. *If the sound is high energy,* cq *is usually used instead of* qq.

Repeat: questo quota quattro acqua annacquato sequenza sequoia

E. *Write the following. The words will be repeated so that you can check your accuracy.*

________________ ________________ ________________

________________ ________________ ________________

D I C T A T I O N

Listen to the following sentences, then write each sentence during the pause. Each sentence will be repeated so that you can check your accuracy.

1. ____

____

2. ____

____

3. ____

____

4. ____

____

5. ____

____

NAME ______________________ DATE __________ CLASS __________

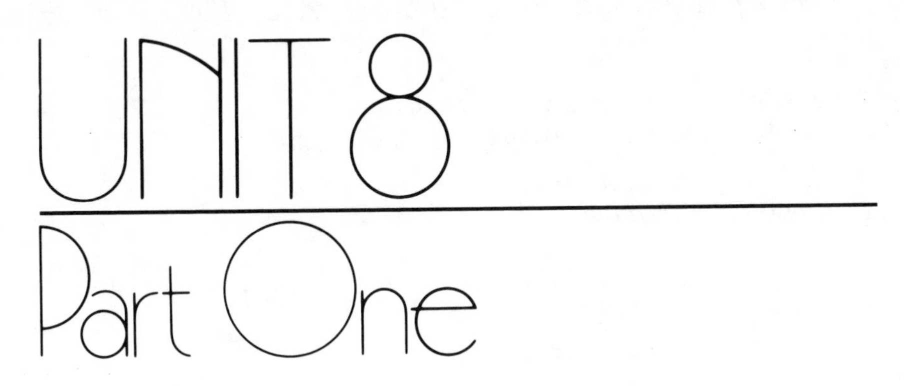

UNIT 8 Part One

D I A L O G U E

Listen to the following dialogue.

LA MUSICA

Laura, Gianna e il professor Bianchi, un professore di chimica e amico di famiglia, parlano di musica.

Gianna: Le piace la musica folk, professore?
Professore: Mi piacciono molti cantanti, ma preferisco la musica classica o il jazz.
Gianna: E a te quale musica piace? Ti piace il rock?
Laura: A me la musica piace tutta. Ma soprattutto mi piace suonare la chitarra e cantare.

Now repeat each sentence after the speaker.

G R A M M A T I C A

I. PRONOUNS AS DIRECT OR INDIRECT OBJECT: CONJUNCTIVE AND DISJUNCTIVE PRONOUNS

A. *In the following sentences substitute conjunctive pronouns for the noun objects. There may be two correct answers. Then repeat the correct sentence after the speaker gives it.*

Example: Insegna l'inglese al giornalaio.
Gli insegna l'inglese.

1. .... 3. .... 5. ....

2. .... 4. ....

B. *In the following sentences substitute the correct conjunctive pronoun before* piacere. *Then repeat the correct sentence after the speaker gives it.*

Examples: 1. Al professore piace la musica classica.
Gli piace la musica classica.

2. A noi piace la chitarra.
Ci piace la chitarra.

1. .... 3. .... 5. ....

2. .... 4. ....

C. *Answer the following questions using the correct conjunctive pronoun and* bene. *Then repeat the correct sentence after the speaker gives it.*

Example: Conosci il professore?
Lo conosco bene.

1. .... 3. .... 5. ....

2. .... 4. ....

D. *Answer the following questions using the correct conjunctive pronoun and the words given. Then repeat the correct sentence after the speaker gives it.*

Example: Dove vedi i tuoi amici?
al bar di via Torino
Li vedo al bar di via Torino.

1. .... 3. .... 5. ....

2. .... 4. ....

E. *Change the following sentences from the negative to the affirmative. Then substitute the correct conjunctive pronoun as object. Repeat the correct sentence after the speaker gives it.*

Example: Questi studenti non vogliono imparare l'italiano.
Questi studenti vogliono imparare l'italiano.
Questi studenti lo vogliono imparare.

1. .... 3. .... 5. ....

2. .... 4. ....

NAME ______________________ DATE __________ CLASS __________

II. THE VERB *PIACERE* AND VERBS TAKING THE SAME CONSTRUCTION: *SERVIRE, MANCARE, OCCORRERE, DISPIACERE, INTERESSARE, ESSERE SIMPATICO*, ETC.

A. *Create new sentences by substituting in the base sentence the words given.*

1. Example: A me piace la musica folk.
   studentesse
   Alle studentesse piace la musica folk.

   ....

   ....

2. Example: Ai giovani interessa la politica.
   lei
   A lei interessa la politica.

   ....

   ....

B. *Change the following sentences by substituting conjunctive pronouns for the disjunctive pronoun expressions. Then repeat the correct sentence after the speaker gives it.*

Example: A me piace la musica folk.
Mi piace la musica folk.

1. .... 3. .... 5. ....

2. .... 4. ....

C. *Create new sentences by substituting in the base sentence the words given.*

1. Example: Gli piace l'opera.
   parlare al telefono
   Gli piace parlare al telefono.

   ....

   ....

2. Example: Non le piace suonare la chitarra.
   i dischi
   Non le piacciono i dischi.

   ....

   ....

D. *Create new sentences by substituting in the base sentence the subjects given.*

1. Example: La signora mi è antipatica.
   le signore
   Le signore mi sono antipatiche.

   ....

   ....

2. Example: Quel signore vi è simpatico.
   gli americani
   Gli americani vi sono simpatici.

   ....

   ....

E. *Make the following sentences negative. Then change them to the compound past. Repeat the correct sentence after the speaker gives it.*

Example: Le servono i dischi.
Non le servono i dischi.
Non le sono serviti i dischi.

1. .... 3. ....

2. .... 4. ....

NAME ______________________ DATE ____________ CLASS ____________

UNIT 8

Part Two

G R A M M A T I C A

INTERROGATIVES: *QUALE, CHE, QUANTO*

A. *Create new questions by substituting in the base question the words given.*

1. Example: Quale giornale vuoi?
   libri
   Quali libri vuoi?

   ....

   ....

2. Example: Che musica ti piace?
   programmi
   Che programmi ti piacciono?

   ....

   ....

3. Example: Quanto olio desidera?
   gettoni
   Quanti gettoni desidera?

   ....

   ....

B. *Begin the following questions with the correct form of* quanto *as in the example. Then repeat the complete question after the speaker gives it.*

Example: libri hai comprato?
Quanti libri hai comprato?

1. .... 4. .... 7. ....

2. .... 5. .... 8. ....

3. .... 6. ....

IV. REVIEW OF PRONOUNS

A. *In the following sentences use the correct conjunctive pronoun in place of the noun object. Then repeat the correct sentence after the speaker gives it.*

Example: Gianna non porta le gonne lunghe.
Gianna non le porta lunghe.

1. .... 3. .... 5. ....

2. .... 4. .... 6. ....

LISTENING / COMPREHENSION

Listen to the following dialogue.

DOVE ANDARE A FAR SPESE

Laura chiede a Gianna dov'è meglio comprare alcune cose.

Laura: Mi piace molto come vesti. Dove compri i vestiti?
Gianna: Come vedi, io porto solo roba sportiva: gonne, pantaloni, camicette e golf.
Laura: Dove li compri?
Gianna: Mah! Non ho un negozio di abbigliamento speciale. Compro quasi tutto ai grandi magazzini. Sono più economici.
Laura: I grandi magazzini vendono anche camicie e giacche da uomo?
Gianna: Certamente. Lí trovi anche collant, guanti, calzini da uomo e calze da donna. E trovi tutto a buon mercato.
Laura: Anche le scarpe?
Gianna: No, le scarpe è meglio comprarle in un negozio di calzature.
Laura: Grazie. Ho imparato molto!
Gianna: A proposito, tu dove compri le riviste straniere?
Laura: In centro. I giornalai e i librai di quartiere non le hanno. Non hanno neanche i giornali o i libri stranieri.
Gianna: Il giornalaio del tuo quartiere li ha.
Laura: Ogni tanto. Come lo sai? Conosci il signor Mari? Figurati che mi ha chiesto di insegnargli l'inglese! Mi è cosí simpatico!

NAME ______________________ DATE ____________ CLASS __________

Gianna: Davvero? Perché non insegni l'inglese anche a me?
Laura: Perché no? Però devi leggere un libro al giorno come fa il signor Mari.

QUESTIONS

You will hear six questions about the dialogue you have just heard. Indicate the correct answer to each question by circling the letter before it. You will hear each question twice.

1. ....

a. al mercato

b. in un negozio di abbigliamento

c. ai grandi magazzini

2. ....

a. perché hanno tutto

b. perché sono più economici

c. perché non sono a buon mercato

3. ....

a. le scarpe

b. le gonne

c. i pantaloni

4. ....

a. i giornali

b. i calzini

c. i guanti

5. ....

a. di leggergli un libro inglese

b. di insegnargli l'inglese

c. di comprargli una rivista

6. ....

a. economico

b. straniero

c. simpatico

INTONATION AND SOUND DISCRIMINATION

A. Repeat the following progressive variations.

1. porto solo gonne
porto solo gonne e pantaloni
porto solo gonne, pantaloni e camicette
porto solo gonne, pantaloni, camicette e golf

2. i giornalai di quartiere hanno le riviste
i giornalai di quartiere non hanno le riviste
i giornalai di quartiere non hanno le riviste e i giornali
i giornalai di quartiere non hanno le riviste e i giornali stranieri

3. dove compri i libri?
   dove compri i libri stranieri?
   tu, dove compri i libri stranieri?

B. *You will hear some short sentences using the pronouns* li, gli *or* le. *Repeat the sentence after the speaker, then circle whichever pronoun you have heard. You will hear each sentence twice.*

1. .... li gli le
2. .... li gli le
3. .... li gli le
4. .... li gli le
5. .... li gli le
6. .... li gli le

SOUND DISCRIMINATION

You will hear seven sentences on tape. After listening to each, indicate the one you heard by circling the letter before it. You will hear each sentence twice.

1. a. Rendetegli il libro!
   b. Prendetegli il libro!

2. a. Cantiamo tutti insieme!
   b. Contiamo tutti insieme!

3. a. Ha intenzione di farlo.
   b. Non fa attenzione.

4. a. Volete qualcosa di bello?
   b. Vedete qualcosa di bello?

5. a. Questo vestito è molto chiaro.
   b. Questo vestito è molto caro.

6. a. Ci sono molte colline.
   b. Ci sono molte collane.

7. a. È arrivato il nonno.
   b. È arrivato nono.

P R O N U N C I A T I O N

SOUND AND SPELLING OF THE CONSONANT /č/

A. *The sound /č/ in Italian is pronounced as in English. However, like all Italian consonants, it may be uttered with high energy or low energy. All vowels preceding high energy /č/ become short; all vowels preceding low energy /č/ are long. Remember to give short and long vowels exactly the same sound, varying only the length. Contrast high and low energy /č/ in the following pairs.*

Repeat: ceci/cecio . . . maciullare/macero . . . ciancia/cioè . . .
dolci/luce . . . acero/acceso . . . lucio/luccio . . .
lécito/l'èccito . . . micia/miccia . . . cuocio/coccio

NAME ______________________ DATE ____________ CLASS ____________

Now pronounce this sound in phrases. Repeat:

un acero lucido   accètta la pace   lo féce con l'accétta

accipicchia che acino   è un fucile che uccide

B. *The sound /č/ has two possible spellings:* c *before* e *or* i, *and* ci *before* a, o, *or* u. *As with most Italian consonants, if /č/ is uttered with high energy, the* c *is doubled. Read the following words. These words will be repeated so that you can check your pronunciation.*

Repeat:	lacci	céna	chioccia	cinema	faccia
	leccio	ciurma	acciacchi	cacio	
	cincischia	céci	chiocciola	cucina	
	ciuco	acacia	Cecco	Cicerone	

C. *Write the following words. They will be repeated so that you can check your accuracy.*

________________ ________________ ________________

________________ ________________ ________________

________________ ________________ ________________

________________ ________________ ________________

________________ ________________ ________________

____

D I C T A T I O N

Listen to the following sentences. Write each sentence during the pause. Each sentence will be repeated so that you can check your accuracy.

1. ____

____

2. ____

____

3. ____

____

4. ____

____

5. ____

____

NAME ______________ DATE __________ CLASS __________

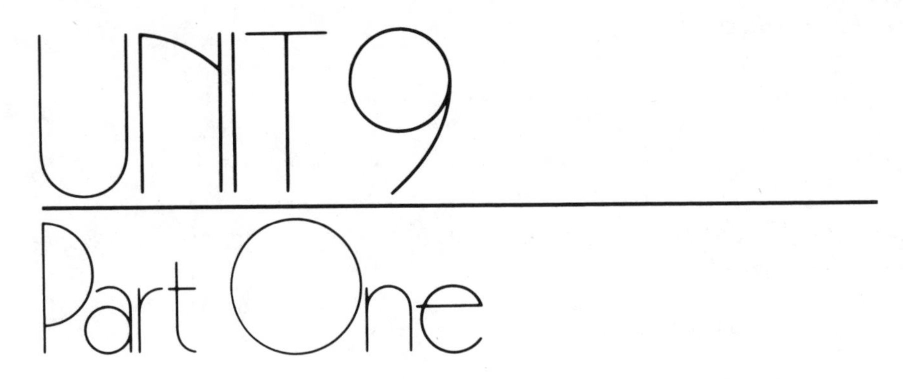

D I A L O G U E

Listen to the complete dialogue.

LA ZIA DI GIACOMO

Laura è andata a trovare la zia di Giacomo.

Zia: Stasera non guardo neanche la televisione. Vado a dormire. Sono stanca e ho sonno.
Laura: Si è alzata presto stamattina?
Zia: No, alle sette come sempre.
Laura: Come passa la mattina, di solito?
Zia: Mi alzo, mi metto la vestaglia, e vado in bagno dove mi lavo, mi vesto e mi pettino. Poi preparo la colazione.

Now repeat each sentence after the speaker.

G R A M M A T I C A

I. REFLEXIVE VERBS

A. *Create new sentences by substituting in the base sentence the correct form of the verbs given.*

1. Example: Le studentesse si alzano.
lavarsi
Le studentesse si lavano.

....

....

2. Example: Mi alzo tardi.
svegliarsi
Mi sveglio tardi.

....

....

B. *Create new sentences by substituting in the base sentence the subjects given.*

1. Example: Mio marito si alza presto.
tu
Ti alzi presto.

....

....

2. Example: Mi sveglio alle sette.
loro
Si svegliano alle sette.

....

....

3. Example: Come si chiama suo marito?
il salumiere
Come si chiama il salumiere?

....

....

C. *Answer the following questions in the affirmative. Then repeat the correct sentence after the speaker gives it.*

Example: Ti addormenti tardi di solito?
Sí, mi addormento tardi di solito.

1. .... 3. .... 5. ....

2. .... 4. ....

D. *Create new sentences by substituting in the base sentence the subjects given.*

1. Example: I miei amici si sono conosciuti un anno fa.
tu e lei
Tu e lei vi siete conosciuti un anno fa.

....

....

NAME ______________________ DATE ____________ CLASS ___________

2. Example: Si sono innamorati e si sono sposati.
voi
Vi siete innamorati e vi siete sposati.

....

....

E. *Change the following sentences into the compound past. Then repeat the correct sentence after the speaker gives it.*

Example: Il mio amico si sposa.
Il mio amico si è sposato.

1. .... 3. .... 5. ....

2. .... 4. ....

II. IMPERSONAL *SI*

A. *Change the following sentences by using impersonal* si *as subject in place of* tutti. *Then repeat the correct sentence after the speaker gives it.*

Example: Tutti studiano l'inglese in Italia.
Si studia l'inglese in Italia.

1. .... 3. .... 5. ....

2. .... 4. .... 6. ....

B. *In the following sentences substitute the subjects supplied for impersonal* si. *Then repeat the correct sentence after the speaker gives it.*

Example: Si studia l'italiano a lezione.
noi
Studiamo l'italiano a lezione.

1. .... 3. .... 5. ....

2. .... 4. ....

III. CONOSCERE AND SAPERE

A. *Create new sentences by substituting in the base sentence the subjects given.*

1. Example: Il professore conosce bene Firenze.
   io
   Conosco bene Firenze.

   ....

   ....

2. Example: Conosco la strada per andare al centro.
   loro
   Conoscono la strada per andare al centro.

   ....

   ....

B. *Answer the following questions in the negative. Then repeat the correct sentence after the speaker gives it.*

Example: Conosci l'amica di Giacomo?
No, non la conosco bene.

1. .... 3. .... 5. ....

2. .... 4. ....

C. *Answer the following questions in the negative using either* sapere *or* conoscere. *Then repeat the correct sentence after the speaker gives it.*

Examples: Luigi? *Non lo conosco.*
La lezione? *Non la sappiamo.*

1. .... 4. .... 6. ....

2. .... 5. .... 7. ....

3. ....

NAME ______________________________ DATE ____________ CLASS __________

UNIT 9
Part Two

G R A M M A T I C A

THE VERB *FARE*

A. *Create new sentences by substituting in the base sentence the subjects given.*

1. Example: La signora Spina fa la spesa alle dieci.
   noi
   Facciamo la spesa alle dieci.

   ....

   ....

2. Example: Mi faccio il bagno tardi.
   loro
   Si fanno il bagno tardi.

   ....

   ....

3. Example: Faccio colazione con gli zii.
   voi
   Fate colazione con gli zii.

   ....

   ....

LISTENING/COMPREHENSION

Listen to the following dialogue.

A FIRENZE

Dopo qualche settimana Carla e Laura s'incontrano in una strada di Firenze.

Laura: Buon giorno signora Bianchi.
Carla: Buon giorno Laura. Perché non ci diamo del tu?
Laura: Perché no? È più semplice.
Carla: Conosci la strada per andare a piazza della Signoria?
Laura: No, Firenze la conosco poco. Però ho una pianta della città.
Carla: Si dice che il centro di Firenze è piccolo come un uovo: non ci si può perdere.
Laura: È vero. Si cammina, si cammina, e ci si trova sempre a piazza del Duomo, a piazza della Signoria o al Ponte Vecchio.
Carla: Il palazzo della Signoria e la cupola del Duomo si vedono anche da lontano.
Laura: Da qui non si vedono. Come si chiama questa strada?
Carla: Veramente non so il nome di questa strada.
Laura: Però sai come si arriva a piazza della Signoria da qui?
Carla: Certamente, si prende quella strada a destra, si va dritti per cento metri fino a via Tornabuoni. Alla seconda traversa, dov'è il semaforo, si gira a sinistra.
Laura: E si è arrivati a piazza della Signoria?
Carla: Sí è facile, non è vero?
Laura: Non è difficile.

QUESTIONS

You will hear six questions about the dialogue you have just heard. Indicate the correct answer to each question by circling the letter before it. You will hear each question twice.

1. ....

   a. in una strada di Roma

   b. a piazza della Signoria

   c. in una strada di Firenze

2. ....

   a. perché la conosce bene

   b. perché la conosce poco

   c. perché conosce la strada per andare a ponte Vecchio

3. ....

   a. molto grande

   b. piccolo come un uovo

   c. non molto piccolo

4. ....

   a. la cupola del Duomo

   b. piazza della Signoria

   c. il ponte Vecchio

NAME ______________________ DATE ____________ CLASS ____________

5. ....

a. una strada

b. una piazza

c. un duomo

6. ....

a. difficile

b. è facile

c. lontano

INTONATION AND SOUND DISCRIMINATION

A. Conoscere *and* sapere. *Repeat the following sentences after the speaker, pronouncing carefully and noticing the use of* conoscere *and* sapere.

1. Conosciamo bene Laura e sappiamo dove abita.
2. Conosco Firenze e so che è piccola.
3. Non conosco quel ristorante ma so che è buono.
4. Conoscete il duomo ma non sapete quanto è vecchio.
5. Conosci l'infermiera ma non sai perché dorme.
6. Conosco il Ponte Vecchio e so come ci si va.

B. *Repeat the following sentences after the speaker and circle* S *if you have heard a statement, or* Q *if a question and also* P *if the sentence is positive,* N *if negative. You will hear each sentence twice.*

1. .... S Q P N
2. .... S Q P N
3. .... S Q P N
4. .... S Q P N
5. .... S Q P N
6. .... S Q P N

C. *Repeat the following sentences after the speaker and circle* F *if they are in formal address,* I *if in informal address. You will hear each question twice.*

1. .... F I
2. .... F I
3. .... F I
4. .... F I
5. .... F I
6. .... F I

P R O N U N C I A T I O N

THE SOUND AND SPELLING OF /g/

A. *The sound /g/ in Italian is pronounced as in English. However, like all Italian consonant sounds, it may be uttered with high energy or low energy. Remember that, as usual for Italian consonants, all vowels preceding high energy /g/ become short, while all vowels preceding low energy /g/ are long. Remember to pronounce all short vowels as distinctly as the corresponding long vowels.*

Repeat: ghiro . . . gusto . . . gola . . . gara . . . guanto . . .
ghetto . . . lago . . . Ugo . . . greco . . . aghi . . .
Ragusa . . . regola . . . margherita . . . aggancio . . .
agguantare . . . agghindare . . . leggo . . . ungo . . .
fuggo . . . fungo

Repeat and contrast: sugo/suggo . . . fuga/fugga . . . lego/leggo . . .
aghino/agghindo . . . regola/reggo . . . fugano/fuggono . . .
sgraziato/aggraziato . . . agonia/aggomitolare

B. *The sound /g/ has two possible spellings:* g *before all consonants and the vowels* a, o *or* u, *and* gh *before* e *or* i. *If the sound /g/ is intense, the* g *is doubled, as occurs with most Italian consonants.*

Repeat the following words. They will be repeated after you, so that you can check if you have read them correctly.

angolo . . . ghianda . . . aggradare . . . aggredire . . . lago . . .
mago . . . ghermine . . . si seggono . . . segano . . . laghi . . .
ripongo . . . ghiaccio . . . ghiotto . . . Guido . . . seghe

C. *Repeat the sound /g/ in phrases. They will be repeated after you, so that you can check your pronunciation.*

sega quell'angolo . . . guida il ghiotto Guido . . . tre maghi in tre
laghi . . .fragole e funghetti . . . ha la gotta in gola? . . .
riponga il granchio . . . il gatto è in fuga

NAME ______________________________ DATE ___________ CLASS ____________

D. *Write the following words. The words will be repeated so that you can check your accuracy.*

____________________ ____________________

____________________ ____________________

____________________ ____________________

____________________ ____________________

____________________ ____________________

D I C T A T I O N

Listen to the following sentences. Write each sentence during the pause. Each sentence will be repeated so that you can check your accuracy.

1. ____

____

2. ____

____

3. ____

____

4. ____

____

5. ____

____

NAME ____________________ DATE __________ CLASS __________

UNIT 10

Part One

D I A L O G U E

Listen to the complete dialogue.

INFORMAZIONI

Giacomo: Scusi, dov'è piazza del Duomo?
Benzinaio: Non è lontano. Come ci va, a piedi o in macchina?
Giacomo: Ci posso andare in macchina?
Benzinaio: Se vuole può andarci, ma non è facile a causa delle strade a senso unico.
Giacomo: Posso parcheggiare a piazza del Duomo?
Benzinaio: Sí, se trova posto al parcheggio.

Now repeat each sentence after the speaker.

G R A M M A T I C A

I. USES OF *CI* AND *NE*

A. *In the following sentences replace the prepositional phrases with* ci. *Then repeat the correct sentence after the speaker gives it.*

Example: Vanno al centro in macchina.
Ci vanno in macchina.

1. ....
2. ....
3. ....
4. ....
5. ....

B. *Change the following sentences by replacing* ci *with the phrases given. Then repeat the correct sentence after the speaker gives it.*

Example: Ci vado a piedi.
al centro
Vado al centro a piedi.

1. .... 3. .... 5. ....

2. .... 4. .... 6. ....

C. *Change the following sentences: substitute* ne *for* da *plus noun. Then repeat the correct sentence after the speaker gives it.*

Example: Mario viene da Milano oggi.
Mario ne viene oggi.

1. .... 3. .... 5. ....

2. .... 4. ....

D. *Change the following sentences: substitute the phrases supplied for* ne. *Then repeat the correct sentence after the speaker gives it.*

Example: Ne discute sempre.
il suo amico
Discute sempre del suo amico.

1. .... 3. .... 5. ....

2. .... 4. ....

Example: Mario ne viene oggi.
Milano
Mario viene da Milano oggi.

1. .... 3. .... 5. ....

2. .... 4. ....

E. *Change the following sentences: substitute* ne *for the noun after the numeral. Then repeat the correct sentence after the speaker gives it.*

Example: Voglio dieci biglietti.
Ne voglio dieci.

1. .... 3. .... 5. ....

2. .... 4. ....

NAME ______________________ DATE ____________ CLASS ____________

F. *Change the following sentences: substitute* ne *for the prepositional phrase. Then repeat the correct sentence during the second pause.*

Example: Compra un chilo di pane.
Ne compra un chilo.

1. .... 3. .... 5. ....

2. .... 4. ....

II. CONJUNCTIVE PRONOUNS WITH MODAL VERBS

A. *Change the following sentences by inserting the correct form of the modal verb supplied. Then repeat the correct sentence after the speaker gives it.*

Example: Il professore ne scrive molti.
dovere
Il professore ne deve scrivere molti.

1. .... 3. .... 5. ....

2. .... 4. ....

B. *Answer the following questions as in the example, attaching all pronouns to the infinitive. Then repeat the correct sentence after the speaker gives it.*

Example: Gli vuole telefonare oggi?
No, vuole telefonargli domani.

1. .... 3. .... 5. ....

2. .... 4. ....

III. FORMAL IMPERATIVE FOR THE THREE CONJUGATIONS, REGULAR AND IRREGULAR VERBS

A. *Change the following statements into formal commands. Then repeat the correct sentence after the speaker gives it.*

Example: Cambia gli spicci per il suo amico.
Cambi gli spicci per il Suo amico!

1. .... 4. .... 7. ....

2. .... 5. .... 8. ....

3. .... 6. ....

B. *Create new sentences by substituting in the base sentence the formal imperatives of the verbs given.*

1. Example: Parli al suo amico!
   scrivere una lettera
   Scriva una lettera al suo amico!

   ....

   ....

2. Example: Parlino con i Loro amici!
   partire
   Partano con i Loro amici!

   ....

   ....

IV. IRREGULAR VERBS: *TENERE, VENIRE, SALIRE, SEDERSI, USCIRE*

A. *Create new sentences by substituting in the base sentence the words given.*

1. Example: L'ospite viene da Roma oggi, ne viene alle sette.
   gli ospiti
   Gli ospiti vengono da Roma oggi, ne vengono alle sette.

   ....

   ....

2. Example: Il mio amico è sull'autobus e tiene un posto libero.
   voi
   Siete sull'autobus e tenete un posto libero.

   ....

   ....

3. Example: Salgo sull'autobus, ci salgo alla fermata.
   gli stranieri
   Gli stranieri salgono sull'autobus, ci salgono alla fermata.

   ....

   ....

4. Example: Esco con gli amici e mi siedo al bar.
   tu
   Esci con gli amici e ti siedi al bar.

   ....

   ....

NAME ______________________ DATE ____________ CLASS ___________

UNIT 10

Part Two

G R A M M A T I C A

VERB REVIEW

A. *Create new sentences by substituting in the base sentence the subjects given.*

1. Example: Mi fa un piacere, mi cambia un biglietto da mille lire.
   gli amici
   Gli amici mi fanno un piacere, mi cambiano un biglietto da mille lire.

   ....

   ....

2. Example: Prende la strada a destra e va al parcheggio.
   il vigile
   Il vigile prende la strada a destra e va al parcheggio.

   ....

   ....

3. Example: Esco presto e ritorno alle sei.
   il medico
   Il medico esce presto e ritorna alle sei.

   ....

   ....

L I S T E N I N G / C O M P R E H E N S I O N

Listen to the following dialogue.

A MILANO

Giacomo è in un quartiere sconosciuto di Milano e chiede informazioni ad un passante.

Giacomo:	Scusi, per andare al museo di Brera devo prendere un autobus o la metropolitana?
Passante:	Questa è la fermata dell'autobus che ci passa davanti. Può anche prendere quell'autobus che ci passa dietro.
Giacomo:	Il biglietto lo faccio sull'autobus?
Passante:	Salga sull'autobus e domandi a qualcuno. A volte c'è il bigliettaio e a volte c'è una macchinetta per i biglietti.

Giacomo sale sull'autobus.

Giacomo:	Scusi, signore, quanto costa il biglietto?
Signore:	Metta una moneta da cinquanta lire e il biglietto viene fuori da questa fessura.
Giacomo:	Mi cambi un biglietto da mille lire, sia gentile. Non ho soldi spicci.
Signore:	Mi dispiace ma non ho da cambiarLe. Tenga una moneta da cinquanta lire.
Giacomo:	Grazie. Prenda un gettone del telefono in cambio.
Signore:	Mi faccia il piacere. Non ci pensi neppure.
Giacomo:	Si sieda prego, c'è un posto libero.
Signore:	No grazie, preferisco stare in piedi. Tra poco scendo.
Giacomo:	Tra quante fermate devo scendere per il museo?
Signore:	Fra tre o quattro. Alla Scala ci è già andato? Lo sa che è forse il teatro lirico più famoso del mondo?
Giacomo:	Ci vado domani. Oggi vado al museo di Brera, ieri sono andato al Duomo...
Signore:	Permesso, permesso? Devo scendere. ArrivederLa. Questa è la mia fermata.

QUESTIONS

You will hear six questions about the dialogue you have just heard. Indicate the correct answer to the questions by circling the letter before it. You will hear each question twice.

1. ....

   a. mette una moneta da cinquanta lire
   b. chiede informazioni a un passante
   c. compra un biglietto

2. ....

   a. una persona che vende i biglietti
   b. una macchinetta per i biglietti
   c. una persona che va in autobus

NAME ______________________________ DATE ____________ CLASS ___________

3. ....

a. centocinquanta lire

b. un gettone

c. cinquanta lire

4. ....

a. un biglietto da mille lire

b. un gettone

c. una moneta da cinquanta lire

5. ....

a. perché tra poco scende

b. perché c'è un posto libero

c. perché vuole sedersi

6. ....

a. un museo

b. un teatro lirico

c. un quartiere di Milano

INTONATION AND SOUND DISCRIMINATION

A. *Repeat the following progressive variations.*

a. mi cambi mille lire
mi cambi un biglietto da mille lire
mi cambi un biglietto da mille lire, sia gentile

b. tra quante fermate devo scendere?
tra quante fermate devo scendere per andare al museo?
tra quante fermate devo scendere per andare al museo di Brera?

c. è andato?
è già andato?
alla Scala è già andato?
alla Scala ci è già andato?

B. *Listen to the following sentences. They will be either statements of fact or formal commands. Repeat each sentence after the speaker, then circle* S *if it is a statement of fact,* FC *if it is a formal command. You will hear each sentence twice.*

1. .... S FC
2. .... S FC
3. .... S FC
4. .... S FC
5. .... S FC
6. .... S FC
7. .... S FC
8. .... S FC

C. *Repeat after the speaker the following sentences using the possessive. Notice the agreement of the possessive with its noun as you copy the speaker's pronunciation.*

1. Sono Anna; ecco il mio vestito e le mie scarpe.
2. Sono Francesco; ecco la mia televisione e il mio programma.
3. Sto molto male: ecco il mio dottore e le mie infermiere.
4. Ecco la mia famiglia: mio zio, mia zia e i miei nipoti.
5. Ecco la mia famiglia: mio marito, le mie figlie e mio figlio.

PRONUNCIATION

A. *The sound /ǧ/ in Italian is pronounced like in English. However, as for all Italian consonant sounds, it may be uttered with high energy or low energy. As usual, all vowels preceding high energy /ǧ/ become short; all vowels preceding low energy /ǧ/ are long. Remember to pronounce long and short vowels exactly the same, varying only the length.*

Repeat: giro gesto giara gioco giusto

magico angelo fagiolo saggio reggia

aggiustare

Repeat and contrast these pairs: agio/aggio regio/reggia

magi/maggi mogio/moggio legione/leggenda

rugiada/rugge bigi/infiggi

B. *The /ǧ/ sound has two possible spellings:* g *before* i *or* e *and* gi *before* a, o, *or* u. *If the sound /ǧ/ is high-energy, the* g *is doubled, as with most Italian consonants.*

Repeat these words after the speaker. They will be repeated after you so that you can check if you have read them accurately.

Gino Giulio Gianna getto raggiro

giallo grigio gigaro gigione megera

giogo giorgina aggiornare gigante

faggio seggi leggiamo

Pronounce this sound in phrases.

aggiusta la giara è un giardino giallo gira e regira

maggio non è bigio si gela in gennaio

agevolano la legge

NAME ________________________ DATE ____________ CLASS ____________

C. *Write the following words. The words will be repeated so that you can check your accuracy.*

______________ ______________ ______________

______________ ______________ ______________

______________ ______________ ______________

______________ ______________ ______________

____

DICTATION

Listen to the following sentences. Write each sentence during the pause. Each sentence will be repeated so that you can check your accuracy.

1. ____

____

2. ____

____

3. ____

____

4. ____

____

5. ____

____

NAME ______________________ DATE ____________ CLASS ____________

UNIT 11 Part One

D I A L O G U E

Listen to the following dialogue.

PROGETTI PER IL FUTURO

Laura e Giacomo parlano del loro futuro.

Giacomo: Da quanto tempo sei in Italia, Laura?
Laura: Da quattro mesi. Sono arrivata in settembre e ora siamo in dicembre.
Giacomo: Quando tornerai negli Stati Uniti?
Laura: A giugno, purtroppo.
Giacomo: Che farai quando tornerai a casa?
Laura: Non so ancora.

Now repeat each sentence after the speaker.

G R A M M A T I C A

I. THE FUTURE

A. *Create new sentences by substituting in the base sentence the subjects supplied.*

1. Example: Comprerà i vestiti al centro.
gli ospiti
Gli ospiti compreranno i vestiti al centro.

....

....

2. Example: Domani leggerò questi libri.
il professore
Domani il professore leggerà questi libri.

....

....

3. Example: Finirò la lezione tra un'ora.
tu
Finirai la lezione tra un'ora.

....

....

B. *Create new sentences by substituting in the base sentence the future of the verbs supplied.*

1. Example: Verrò domani.
cantare
Canterò domani.

....

....

2. Example: Partiremo fra sei mesi.
stare in Italia
Staremo in Italia fra sei mesi.

....

....

3. Example: Rimarrete a Roma in ottobre.
dipingere quadri
Dipingerete quadri in ottobre.

....

....

C. *Change the following sentences from present to future and add the adverbs supplied. Then repeat the correct sentence after the speaker gives it.*

Example: Faccio oroscopi a tutti.
domani
Farò oroscopi a tutti domani.

1. .... 3. .... 5. ....

2. .... 4. ....

NAME ______________________ DATE ____________ CLASS ____________

II. NEGATIVES

A. *Change the following sentences from affirmative to negative by using the negative elements supplied. Then repeat the correct sentence after the speaker gives it.*

Example: Ti sposerai.
non-mai
Non ti sposerai mai.

1. .... 3. .... 5. ....

2. .... 4. ....

III. ADVERBS

A. *Change the following adjectives into the corresponding adverbs ending in* -mente. *Then repeat both adjective and adverb after the speaker gives the correct adverb.*

Example: stanco
stancamente

....

....

B. *Create new sentences by substituting in the base sentence the adverbs supplied.*

1. Example: La vostra casa è qui.
all'angolo
La vostra casa è all'angolo.

....

....

2. Example: Il medico è sempre stanco.
senza dubbio
Il medico è senza dubbio stanco.

....

....

C. *Create new sentences by substituting in the base sentence the adverbs formed from the adjectives supplied.*

1. Example: Il pianista suona bene.
   facile
   Il pianista suona facilmente.

   ....

   ....

IV. INVARIABLE NOUNS

A. *Change the following sentences from singular to plural. Then repeat the correct sentence after the speaker gives it.*

Example: Quella città italiana è bella.
Quelle città italiane sono belle.

1. .... 4. .... 6. ....

2. .... 5. .... 7. ....

3. ....

NAME ______________________________ DATE ____________ CLASS ___________

UNIT 11

Part Two

G R A M M A T I C A

TENSE AND VERB REVIEW

A. *Create new sentences by substituting in the base sentence the future of the verbs supplied.*

1. Example: Sicuramente le cose non andranno cosí.
   finire
   Sicuramente le cose non finiranno cosí.

   ....

   ....

2. Example: Hai scritto ieri o scriverai piú tardi?
   cantare
   Hai cantato ieri o canterai piú tardi?

   ....

   ....

B. *Answer the following questions as in the example. Then repeat the correct sentence after the speaker gives it.*

Example: Quando sei nata?
Sono nata il 9 maggio.

1. .... 3. ....

2. .... 4. ....

C. *Change the following questions from singular to plural. Then repeat the correct sentence after the speaker gives it.*

Example: Sei razionale o un sognatore?
Siete razionali o dei sognatori?

1. .... 3. ....

2. .... 4. ....

L I S T E N I N G / C O M P R E H E N S I O N

Listen to the following dialogue.

VENEZIA

Gianna e la madre di Giacomo, la signora Fini, parlano di Venezia.

Signora Fini: Ho risposto a Giacomo con una lunga lettera di tre fogli, sei pagine in tutto.
Gianna: Sei pagine! Sarà pesante.
Signora Fini: Eccola! La busta è pronta, c'è anche l'indirizzo. Ci manca solo il francobollo. Da quanto ci vorrà?
Gianna: Mi faccia sentire il peso. Non è pesante. Ha usato carta leggera! Un francobollo da centosettanta lire è sufficiente.
Signora Fini: Me la spedisci quando esci per favore?
Gianna: Volentieri. Dove sarà Giacomo ora?
Signora Fini: A Venezia. Sono sicura che è già arrivato.
Gianna: Gli piacerà? Venezia è una città morta d'inverno. Non c'è nessuno, vero?
Signora Fini: In autunno e in inverno naturalmente non è mai viva come in primavera o in estate quando ci sono i turisti.
Gianna: Ma non è triste?
Signora Fini: In questa stagione Venezia, io la trovo affascinante. Ha un'aria misteriosa. Come sai, a Venezia non ci sono mai rumori né di macchine né di autobus. Si sentono solo voci umane.
Gianna: Ci dev'essere una grande pace e tranquillità!
Signora Fini: Oh sí, ed è bello vedere i vaporetti e le gondole che scivolano silenziosi lungo i canali e spariscono nella nebbia sotto i ponti.
Gianna: Ma se c'è la nebbia non si vedrà niente.
Signora Fini: Questo è il fascino di Venezia. Quando c'è la nebbia, i palazzi, le chiese, i ponti che sono splendidi, si vedono come dietro ad un velo.
Gianna: Signora, ma Lei è una vera sognatrice, una romantica.

NAME ______________________ DATE ____________ CLASS ____________

QUESTIONS

You will hear six questions about the dialogue. Indicate the correct answer to each question by circling the letter before it. You will hear each question twice.

1. ....

   a. sei fogli

   b. sei pagine

   c. tutte le pagine

2. ....

   a. l'indirizzo

   b. la busta

   c. il francobollo

3. ....

   a. in primavera quando ci sono i turisti

   b. in estate quando è viva

   c. in inverno quando non c'è nessuno

4. ....

   a. trova Venezia affascinante

   b. ci sono molti rumori

   c. si sentono gli autobus nelle strade

5. ....

   a. le voci umane che spariscono

   b. la nebbia che non permette di vedere niente

   c. i vaporetti e le gondole che spariscono sotto i ponti

6. ....

   a. che è una persona misteriosa

   b. che è una romantica

   c. che ha molto fascino

INTONATION AND SOUND DISCRIMINATION

A. *Repeat the following questions after the speaker, pronouncing carefully and using question intonation.*

1. .... 3. .... 5. ....

2. .... 4. .... 6. ....

B. The following sentences have their verbs in the future tense. Repeat each sentence after the speaker, then circle the subject of the verb. You will hear each sentence twice.

1. .... io tu lei/lui noi voi loro

2. .... io tu lei/lui noi voi loro

3. .... io tu lei/lui noi voi loro

4. .... io tu lei/lui noi voi loro

5. .... io tu lei/lui noi voi loro

6. .... io tu lei/lui noi voi loro

C. Invariable nouns are alike in singular and plural, but their articles and adjectives change. Repeat the following sentences after the speaker, then circle S if the invariable noun is singular, P if it is plural. You will hear each sentence twice.

1. .... S P 4. .... S P

2. .... S P 5. .... S P

3. .... S P 6. .... S P

P R O N U N C I A T I O N

THE SOUND AND SPELLING OF /š/

A. The consonant /š/ is pronounced as in English. This sound has only one level of energy in Italian. Repeat the following words:

sciame sciocco sci scelto sciuscià
mesce fasciame uscio fascino esce

B. The consonant /š/ has two possible spellings: sc before e or i, and sci before a, o, u, and sometimes e. Repeat the following words. These words will be repeated after you so that you can check your pronunciation.

asceta moscio prescelto Cascia uscita
fascicolo ganascia scienziato scía scià
fisciú

Note carefully that while sc is pronounced /š/ before e or i, sc before any other letter, vowel or consonant, is pronounced /sk/. Sch is pronounced /sk/. This spelling is used to give the sound /sk/ before e or i. Repeat the following pairs after the speaker, contrasting /š/ and /sk/.

NAME ______________________ DATE ____________ CLASS ____________

Follow the written words in your manual as you speak.

mescio/mescolo esce/esca lisci/Ischia usciolo/pascolo
miscela/mischia sciorinare/schiodare lascia/maschera
viscere/vischio

Practice the sounds in phrases. Repeat the following phrases after the speaker. They will be repeated after you so that you can check your pronunciation.

lascia l'esca le visciole non sono viscide il visconte è
prosciolto mesci la miscela di pesche schioda l'uscio
esce con l'esca

C. *Write the following words. Each will be repeated so that you can check your accuracy.*

____________ ____________ ____________

____________ ____________ ____________

____

D I C T A T I O N

Listen to the following sentences. Then write each sentence during the pause. The sentence will be repeated so that you can check your accuracy.

1. ______________________________

____

2. ______________________________

____

3. ______________________________

____

4. ______________________________

____

5. ______________________________

____

NAME ______________________ DATE ____________ CLASS ____________

UNIT 12

Part One

D I A L O G U E

Listen to the following dialogue.

RICORDI DEL PASSATO

Dopo aver pranzato, Sergio e Giacomo parlano dei tempi passati.

Sergio: Noi ci siamo conosciuti da grandi al Liceo, vero? Tu com'eri da bambino?

Giacomo: Mah! Ero un tipo tranquillo e silenzioso. Leggevo sempre libri di geografia, di scienze e d'avventure. Vivevo in un mondo tutto mio. E tu da piccolo com'eri?

Sergio: Io ero tutto il contrario. Giocavo sempre alla guerra, a guardie e ladri, a palla.

Now repeat each sentence after the speaker.

G R A M M A T I C A

I. PRONOUN GROUPS

A. *In the following sentences substitute the correct pronoun for the noun object. Then repeat the correct sentence after the speaker gives it.*

Example: Ci mette il vino.
Ce lo mette.

1. .... 3. .... 5. ....

2. .... 4. .... 6. ....

B. *Answer the following questions using pronoun groups as in the example. Then repeat the correct sentence after the speaker gives it.*

Example: Si ricorda la frutta?
Sí, me la ricordo.

1. .... 3. .... 5. ....

2. .... 4. ....

C. *Create new sentences by substituting in the base sentence the subjects supplied. Make all necessary changes.*

1. Example: Giacomo se ne va a casa.
io
Me ne vado a casa.

....

....

2. Example: Se ne vuole stare qui.
i compagni di scuola
I compagni di scuola se ne vogliono stare qui.

....

....

D. *Change the following sentences by attaching all pronouns to the infinitive. Then repeat the correct sentence after the speaker gives it.*

Example: Glielo posso dire adesso.
Posso dirglielo adesso.

1. .... 4. .... 6. ....

2. .... 5. .... 7. ....

3. ....

II. IMPERATIVE: INFORMAL COMMANDS

A. *Create new sentences by substituting in the base sentence the familiar imperative of the verbs supplied.*

1. Example: Vieni subito!
leggere
Leggi subito!

....

....

NAME ________________________ DATE ____________ CLASS ___________

2. Example: Venite subito!
leggere
Leggete subito!

....

....

B. *Change the following statements into first-person commands. Then repeat the correct sentence after the speaker gives it.*

Example: Ce ne andiamo alla stazione.
Andiamocene alla stazione!

1. .... 3. .... 5. ....

2. .... 4. ....

C. *Make the following informal commands negative. Then repeat the correct sentence after the speaker gives it.*

Examples: Mettetegli la benzina!
Non mettetegli la benzina!

Parla al telefono!
Non parlare al telefono!

1. .... 3. .... 5. ....

2. .... 4. .... 6. ....

D. *Change the following formal commands to familiar commands. Then repeat the correct sentence after the speaker gives it.*

Example: Ci versi un bicchiere di vino!
Versaci un bicchiere di vino!

1. .... 3. ....

2. .... 4. ....

Example: Ci versino un bicchiere di vino!
Versateci un bicchiere di vino!

1. .... 3. ....

2. .... 4. ....

E. *Change the following negative commands into positive commands. Then repeat the correct sentence after the speaker gives it.*

Example: Non suonare il piano!
Suona il piano!

1. .... 3. .... 5. ....

2. .... 4. ....

III. AGREEMENT OF THE PAST PARTICIPLE IN THE COMPOUND PAST

A. *Change the following sentences by making the direct object a pronoun; make the past participle agree with it. Then repeat the correct sentence after the speaker gives it.*

Example: Ti ha chiesto la rivista.
Te l'ha chiesta.

1. .... 3. .... 5. ....

2. .... 4. ....

B. *Answer the following questions as in the example using pronouns. Then repeat the correct sentence after the speaker gives it.*

Example: Si è ricordato il conto?
No, me lo sono dimenticato.

1. .... 3. .... 5. ....

2. .... 4. ....

C. *Change the following sentences from the present to the compound past; then replace the noun objects with* ne, *making the past participle agree. Repeat the correct sentence after the speaker gives it.*

Example: Compro molti giornali.
Ho comprato molti giornali.
Ne ho comprati molti.

1. .... 3. .... 5. ....

2. .... 4. ....

NAME ______________________ DATE ____________ CLASS ____________

UNIT 12

Part Two

G R A M M A T I C A

THE IMPERFECT TENSE

A. *Create new sentences by substituting in the base sentence the subjects supplied.*

1. Example: La mia amica cantava sempre.
   tu
   Cantavi sempre.

   ....

   ....

2. Example: Non vivevo a Roma tre anni fa.
   le studentesse
   Le studentesse non vivevano a Roma tre anni fa.

   ....

   ....

B. *Change the following sentences from the present to the imperfect. Then repeat the correct sentence after the speaker gives it.*

Example: Parlo mentre tu scrivi.
Parlavo mentre tu scrivevi.

1. .... 3. .... 5. ....

2. .... 4. .... 6. ....

C. *Answer the following questions as in the example, using the imperfect. Repeat the correct sentence after the speaker gives it.*

Example: Giochi con tutti?
No, ma, giocavo con tutti da piccolo.

1. .... 3. .... 5. ....

2. .... 4. ....

LISTENING / COMPREHENSION

Listen to the following dialogue.

AL RISTORANTE CON UN VECCHIO AMICO

Giacomo incontra un vecchio compagno di scuola che vive a Milano.

Sergio: Ciao Giacomo. Ma come, hai la macchina? Non era rotta?
Giacomo: L'ho portata dal meccanico e me l'ha accomodata.
Sergio: Te l'ha accomodata bene?
Giacomo: Perfettamente. È mezzogiorno e mezzo e ho fame. Andiamo a mangiare insieme? Dov'è un buon ristorante?
Sergio: Qui vicino ce ne sono molti. Eccone uno.

Sergio e Giacomo entrano nel ristorante.

Sergio: Sediamoci a questo tavolo lontano dalla porta.
Giacomo: Cameriere, ci porti il menù, per favore.
Sergio: E anche una bottiglia di vino bianco e mezza minerale. Ho molta sete.
Cameriere: Cosa desiderano?
Giacomo: Per primo, io voglio un piatto di tagliatelle al sugo di carne e per secondo un bistecca ai ferri e delle patate fritte.
Sergio: E a me un piatto di spaghetti, del pesce e dell'insalata. Non si dimentichi le posate, almeno le forchette, i coltelli, e i tovaglioli.
Cameriere: Scusino, non Glieli ho ancora messi? Me li sono dimenticati.
Giacomo: Vuoi un po' di vino?
Sergio: Sì, grazie, versamene un mezzo bicchiere.
Giacomo: Sai, questo cameriere è così distratto!
Sergio: Non mi dire! Che manca ancora?
Giacomo: Il pane, il sale, il pepe, l'olio e l'aceto.
Sergio: E il conto.
Giacomo: Quello arriva dopo.

NAME ______________________________ DATE ____________ CLASS ___________

QUESTIONS

You will hear six questions about the dialogue you have just heard. Indicate the correct answer to each question by circling the letter before it. You will hear each question twice.

1. ....

   a. perché è rotta

   b. perché l'ha portata dal meccanico

   c. perché il meccanico gliel'ha accomodata

2. ....

   a. a mezzogiorno e mezzo

   b. in un buon ristorante lí vicino

   c. i due amici hanno fame

3. ....

   a. le posate e i bicchieri

   b. una bottiglia di acqua minerale

   c. mezzo bicchiere di aceto

4. ....

   a. un piatto di tagliatelle con il sugo

   b. della carne e dell'insalata

   c. delle patate e del pesce

5. ....

   a. una tazza di tè al limone

   b. del caffè

   c. mezzo bicchiere di vino

6. ....

   a. Il cameriere è molto distratto.

   b. Il cameriere si dimentica i tovaglioli.

   c. Il cameriere è molto simpatico.

INTONATION AND SOUND DISCRIMINATION

A. *Repeat the following progressive variations.*

a. hai la macchina?
   come hai la macchina?
   ma come hai la macchina?

b. dov'è?
   dov'è un ristorante?
   dov'è un buon ristorante?

c. gliele ho messe?
   non gliele ho messe?
   non gliele ho ancora messe?

B. *Listen to the following questions and tell if they are in formal or informal address. Repeat each question after the speaker, then circle* F *if formal,* I *if informal. You will hear each question twice.*

1.	F	I	4.	F	I
2.	F	I	5.	F	I
3.	F	I	6.	F	I

C. *Tell if the following commands are formal or informal. Repeat each question after the speaker, then circle* F *if formal,* I *if informal. You will hear each sentence twice.*

1.	F	I	5.	F	I
2.	F	I	6.	F	I
3.	F	I	7.	F	I
4.	F	I			

D. *The following sentences have verbs in the imperfect tense. Repeat each sentence after the speaker, then circle the subject of the verb. You will hear each sentence twice.*

1.	io	tu	lei/lui	noi	voi	loro
2.	io	tu	lei/lui	noi	voi	loro
3.	io	tu	lei/lui	noi	voi	loro
4.	io	tu	lei/lui	noi	voi	loro
5.	io	tu	lei/lui	noi	voi	loro
6.	io	tu	lei/lui	noi	voi	loro

PRONUNCIATION

SOUND AND SPELLING OF /s/ AND /z/

A. *The consonant which is written as* s *has two sounds: /s/ and /z/, pronounced like the equivalent English sounds. The sound /s/ occurs when* s *appears at the beginning of a word and is followed either by a vowel or by one of these sounds: /k/, /f/, or /t/. In the middle of a word* s *is pronounced /s/ when it is doubled, when it is followed by an unvoiced consonant, and at times when it occurs between two vowels. The* s *between two vowels is pronounced /s/ or /z/ depending on the region of Italy.*

NAME ______________________ DATE __________ CLASS __________

Repeat: sono sano sino seno suono

spero scarto sferro schiene storto

asino lesso massi fissi rosse

Prussia

B. *The sound /z/ occurs when* s *occurs before one of the following consonant sounds:* /b/, /d/, /g/, /l/, /m/, /n/, /r/, *or* /v/, *and usually when it occurs between two vowels.*

Repeat: sbadato sdentato sgolare sgelo

slegato smaniare snodare srotola

sventolare rosa muso asola dose

resina

Now repeat the following words contrasting low-energy and high-energy /s/. The sound /z/ never occurs with high energy. Each pair of words will be read after you so that you can check your accuracy.

mese/messe resa/ressa raso/rassoda

risa/rissa posa/possa musulmano/ussaro

Repeat the following sentences. Each sentence will be read after you so that you can check your pronunciation.

la rosa è rossa spero che sgeli subito si è sgolato

ha snodato lo spago si sono resi conto della ressa

Elisa è all'asilo ti assiste Rosina

C. *Write the following words. Each word will be repeated so that you can check your accuracy.*

______________ ______________

______________ ______________

______________ ______________

______________ ______________

______________ ______________

______________ ______________

______________ ______________

DICTATION

Listen to the following sentences. Then write each sentence during the pause. The sentence will be repeated so that you can check your accuracy.

1. ____________________

   ____

2. ____________________

   ____

3. ____________________

   ____

4. ____________________

   ____

5. ____________________

   ____

NAME ______________________ DATE ____________ CLASS __________

UNIT 13

Part One

DIALOGUE

Listen to the following dialogue.

UN ALBERGO DI VENEZIA

Giacomo va in un albergo a Venezia.

Giacomo: Vorrei una stanza singola senza bagno.
Albergatore: Mi dispiace, quelle senza bagno sono tutte occupate. Gliene posso dare una con il bagno o con la doccia.
Giacomo: Quali costano di più?
Albergatore: Quelle con il bagno sono migliori delle altre. Sono più grandi e più luminose, e naturalmente sono anche più care.

Now repeat each sentence after the speaker.

GRAMMATICA

I. MORE COMPARATIVES WITH *PIÙ* AND *MENO*

A. *Change the following sentences from the imperfect to the present, adding* più. *Then repeat the correct sentence after the speaker gives it.*

Example: Era già una strada buia.
Ora è più buia.

1. .... 3. .... 5. ....

2. .... 4. ....

B. *Change the following sentences from the imperfect to the present, omitting the subject and adding* meno. *Then repeat the correct sentence after the speaker gives it.*

Example: Ieri il caffè era buono.
Oggi è meno buono.

1. .... 3. .... 5. ....

2. .... 4. ....

C. *Change the following sentences by using* più di *and the words supplied. Then repeat the correct sentence after the speaker gives it.*

Example: La studentessa è magra.
la sua amica
La studentessa è più magra della sua amica.

1. .... 3. .... 5. ....

2. .... 4. ....

D. *Change the following sentences by adding* meno di *and the words supplied. Then repeat the correct sentence after the speaker gives it.*

Example: La studentessa è magra.
la sua amica
La studentessa è meno magra della sua amica.

1. .... 3. .... 5. ....

2. .... 4. ....

E. *Make one sentence out of the two given, using* più di *as in the example. Then repeat the correct sentence after the speaker gives it.*

Example: Laura canta canzoni folk. Anche la sua amica canta canzoni folk.
Laura canta più canzoni folk della sua amica.

1. .... 3. ....

2. .... 4. ....

F. *Make one sentence out of the two given, using* meno di. *Then repeat the correct sentence after the speaker gives it.*

Example: La zia mangia. Anch'io mangio.
La zia mangia meno di me.

1. .... 3. ....

2. .... 4. ....

NAME ________________ DATE ________ CLASS ________

G. *Change the following sentences by substituting* male *for* peggio *and* bene *for* meglio, *as in the example. Then repeat the correct sentence after the speaker gives it.*

Example: Oggi sto peggio di ieri.
Oggi sto male.

1. .... 3. .... 5. ....

2. .... 4. ....

II. COMPARISON WITH *CHE* AND COMPARISON OF EQUALITY WITH *TANTO...QUANTO*

A. *Change the following sentences by adding the element supplied and* piú...che. *Then repeat the correct sentence after the speaker gives it.*

Example: Compro pane oggi.
pasta
Compro piú pane che pasta oggi.

1. .... 3. .... 5. ....

2. .... 4. ....

B. *Change the following sentences by adding the element given and* tanto ...quanto. *Then repeat the correct sentence after the speaker gives it.*

Example: Porta l'ombrello.
l'impermeabile
Porta tanto l'ombrello quanto l'impermeabile.

1. .... 3. .... 5. ....

2. .... 4. ....

III. RELATIVE SUPERLATIVE OF ADJECTIVES

A. *Change the following sentences by adding* piú di *plus the element supplied. Then repeat the correct sentence after the speaker gives it.*

Example: Venezia è una città affascinante.
il mondo
Venezia è la città piú affascinante del mondo.

1. .... 3. .... 5. ....

2. .... 4. .... 6. ....

B. *Change the following sentences by substituting the correct form of* il piú buono *for* il migliore *and of* il meno buono *for* il peggiore. *Then repeat the correct sentence after the speaker gives it.*

Examples: Voglio comprare la pasta migliore.
Voglio comprare la pasta piú buona.

Non voglio comprare la pasta peggiore.
Non voglio comprare la pasta meno buona.

1. ....   4. ....   7. ....

2. ....   5. ....   8. ....

3. ....   6. ....   9. ....

NAME ______________________ DATE ____________ CLASS ____________

GRAMMATICA

IMPERSONAL WEATHER EXPRESSIONS

A. *Create new sentences by substituting in the base sentence the expressions supplied.*

1. Example: Oggi fa freddo ma non piove.
   tira vento
   Oggi tira vento ma non piove.

   ....

   ....

2. Example: Oggi fa freddo ma non deve piovere.
   tira vento
   Oggi fa freddo ma non deve tirare vento.

   ....

   ....

3. Example: Oggi tira vento ma non piove.
   è umido
   Oggi tira vento ma non è umido.

   ....

   ....

B. *You will hear short sentences describing weather conditions. After each sentence you will hear three weather expressions. Cross out the one that does not go with the sentence. You will hear each sentence twice.*

Example: C'è il sole. — Fa caldo. / ~~È nuvolo~~. / Fa bel tempo.

1. .... — È nuvolo. / Fa freddo. / C'è il sole.

2. .... — Nevicava. / Tirava vento. / Faceva caldo.

3. .... — Ci sarà il sole. / Non farà né caldo né freddo. / Pioverà.

4. .... — C'era il sole. / Pioveva. / Faceva freddo.

5. .... — C'è la nebbia. / Fa bel tempo. / È nuvolo.

LISTENING/COMPREHENSION

Listen to the following dialogue.

UNA VISITA ALLA VICINA DEL PRIMO PIANO

Laura va a trovare la signora del primo piano, la signora Spina.

Signora Spina: Venga signorina, entri, si sieda qui sul divano.
Laura: Buon giorno signora, come sta?
Signora Spina: Sto meglio di ieri, grazie. Ieri stavo proprio male. Peggio degli altri giorni.
Laura: Non si preoccupi. Sarà questo brutto tempo.
Signora Spina: Forse. Ma mi dica...come si trova a Roma? Le piace piú di Milwaukee?
Laura: Roma mi piace quanto Milwaukee. La due città sono cosí diverse che non si possono paragonare. Milwaukee non è antica quanto Roma, ma è interessante.
Signora Spina: Le dò ragione. Ha nostalgia di casa?
Laura: Qualche volta penso a casa e mi viene un po'di nostalgia.
Signora Spina: È facile sentirsi depressi quando si è lontani dalla famiglia e dagli amici.
Laura: Ma la depressione non dura molto, mi passa subito.

NAME ______________________ DATE __________ CLASS __________

Signora Spina: Se qualche vola è depressa è perché studia troppo. Deve uscire piú spesso, cantare, divertirsi e stare allegra.

Laura: Non ho molto tempo per divertirmi. Devo dare quattro esami alla prossima sessione. In questi giorni piú che cantare e divertirmi devo studiare.

Signora Spina: Deve studiare cosí intensamente? Che materie studia?

Laura: Ora studio biologia, chimica, matematica e seguo anche un corso di storia dell'arte.

Signora Spina: Vedrà. Gli esami le andranno sicuramente bene.

Laura: Farò del mio meglio.

Signora Spina: Le materie scientifiche le piacciono piú di quelle letterarie?

Laura: No, mi piacciono anche la letteratura, la storia, la psicologia e la sociologia. Ma ora non ho tempo per queste materie.

QUESTIONS

You will hear six questions about the dialogue you have just heard. Indicate the correct answer to each question by circling the letter before it. You will hear each question twice.

1. ....

   a. le chiede come sta

   b. le dice di sedersi sul divano

   c. le dice che sta peggio di ieri

2. ....

   a. le due città non si possono paragonare

   b. Roma è una città antica

   c. Milwaukee è una città interessante

3. ....

   a. ci si sente bene

   b. è molto divertente

   c. viene un po' di nostalgia

4. ....

   a. esce molto spesso

   b. deve studiare molto

   c. è molto depressa

5. ....

   a. l'anno prossimo

   b. alla prossima sessione

   c. quando canta in un concerto

6. ....

   a. le piace la letteratura

   b. segue un corso di storia dell'arte

   c. studia chimica

INTONATION AND SOUND DISCRIMINATION

A. *Repeat the following progressive variations.*

a. venga signorina
venga signorina, entri
venga signorina, entri, si accomodi sulla poltrona
venga signorina, entri, si accomodi sulla poltrona o sul divano

b. studia?
studia molto?
studia molto per l'università?
studia molto per l'università in questi giorni?

B. *Comprehension. Listen to the following situations and decide if one is likely to be depressed or cheerful. Indicate the correct answer by marking the word* allegri *or* depressi.

1.	si è allegri	si è depressi
2.	si è allegri	si è depressi
3.	si è allegri	si è depressi
4.	si è allegri	si è depressi
5.	si è allegri	si è depressi
6.	si è allegri	si è depressi
7.	si è allegri	si è depressi

C. *Tell if the following sentences are statements of fact, questions, or commands. Repeat each after the speaker, copying pronunciation and intonation carefully, then circle* S *for statement,* Q *for question, or* C *for command. You will hear each sentence twice.*

1.	S	Q	C
2.	S	Q	C
3.	S	Q	C
4.	S	Q	C
5.	S	Q	C
6.	S	Q	C
7.	S	Q	C
8.	S	Q	C

NAME ______________________________ DATE ____________ CLASS ___________

PRONUNCIATION

THE SOUND AND SPELLING OF /b/

The consonant /b/ is pronounced as in English. Like most Italian consonants /b/ can be uttered with low energy or high energy. High energy /b/ is represented in writing by a double b. *Remember that before a double consonant all vowels become very short. Also remember that in Italian all short vowels in unstressed syllables are pronounced distinctly, with the same pronunciation as long vowels.*

A. *Repeat the following words:*

basta babbo Sebastiano albero subito

dabbene abbaino berbero burbero buono

botola lobo sbagliato usbergo

Practice high energy and low energy /b/ in contrast. Repeat the following pairs of words. They will be repeated after you so that you can check your pronunciation.

abaco/abbaco tibia/nebbia sebo/ebbro sabato/sabbatico

rubo/rubbio ebano/ebbene obliquo/obbligato

lobato/lobbia tubo/dubbio Libia/fibbia

B. *Practice these sounds in the following phrases. They will be read after you so that you can check your pronunciation.*

Rubò fibbie e rubini una cabina sulla sabbia la nebbia si abbassò a Lisbona una sbornia abbastanza ma non subito abito in un'abitazione bassa una barca d'ebano

C. *Write the following words. Each will be repeated so that you can check your accuracy.*

____________________ ____________________

____________________ ____________________

____________________ ____________________

____________________ ____________________

____________________ ____________________

____

D I C T A T I O N

Listen to the following sentences. Then write each sentence during the pause. The sentence will be repeated so that you can check your accuracy.

1. ______________________________

____

2. ______________________________

____

3. ______________________________

____

4. ______________________________

____

5. ______________________________

____

NAME ______________ DATE ________ CLASS ________

UNIT 14

Part One

D I A L O G U E

Listen to the following dialogue.

BEN TORNATO!

Giacomo incontra Gianna dopo il suo viaggio al nord d'Italia.

Gianna: Ben tornato Giacomo, come va? Quando sei tornato?
Giacomo: Lunedí sera. Che c'è di nuovo?
Gianna: Niente di speciale. Quando sei partito da Venezia?
Giacomo: Sabato pomeriggio: faceva un tempaccio. La notte mi sono fermato in un alberghetto di un paesino di montagna e domenica mattina sono ripartito.
Gianna: Ci hai messo due giorni?
Giacomo: Sí, il viaggio è durato abbastanza.

Now repeat each sentence after the speaker.

G R A M M A T I C A

I. ORDINAL ADJECTIVES

A. *Create new sentences by substituting in the base sentence the noun given.*

Example: È il mio primo libro.
casa
È la mia prima casa.

1. .... 3. .... 5. ....

2. .... 4. ....

B. *In the following sentences, supply the correct ordinal adjective for each month you hear.*

Example: gennaio
Gennaio è il primo mese dell'anno.

....

....

....

C. *Change the following sentences by substituting the ordinal supplied. Then repeat the correct sentence after the speaker gives it.*

Example: Torna nella prima settimana di giugno.
secondo
Torna nella seconda settimana di giugno.

1. .... 3. .... 5. ....

2. .... 4. ....

D. *Answer the following questions as in the example. Then repeat the correct sentence after the speaker gives it.*

Examples: È questa la terza fermata?
No, questa è la seconda fermata.

È questo il decimo libro?
No, questo è il nono libro.

1. .... 3. .... 5. ....

2. .... 4. .... 6. ....

II. THE ABSOLUTE SUPERLATIVE

A. *Create new sentences by substituting in the base sentence the subjects supplied.*

1. Example: Laura è stata bravissima.
lui
È stato bravissimo.

....

....

NAME ______________________ DATE ____________ CLASS ____________

2. Example: Sono riposatissimo adesso.
la studentessa
La studentessa è riposatissima adesso.

....

....

B. *Change the following sentences by using the absolute superlative of the adjective. Then repeat the correct sentence after the speaker gives it.*

Example: Mio zio è alto.
Mio zio è altissimo.

1. .... 3. .... 5. ....

2. .... 4. ....

C. *Change the following sentences: substitute* ottimo *for the superlatives of* buono *and* pessimo *for the superlative of* cattivo. *Then repeat the correct sentence after the speaker gives it.*

Example: Questo programma è molto buono.
Questo programma è ottimo.

Questo programma è molto cattivo.
Questo programma è pessimo.

1. .... 3. .... 5. ....

2. .... 4. ....

III. DIMINUTIVE, AUGMENTATIVE AND PEJORATIVE SUFFIXES: *-ETTO, -INO, -ONE,* AND *-ACCIO*

A. *Create new sentences by substituting in the base sentence diminutive forms of the words supplied.*

1. Example: Ecco un'isoletta.
barca
Ecco una barchetta.

....

....

2. Example: Ecco il paesino.
tesi
Ecco la tesina.

....

....

B. *Respond to the following questions using diminutives as in the example. Then repeat the correct sentence during the second pause.*

Example: Sono piccole queste isole?
Sí, sono delle isolette.

1. .... 3. ....

2. .... 4. ....

Example: Com'è questo paese, grande?
No, è piccolo, è un paesino.

1. .... 3. .... 5. ....

2. .... 4. ....

C. *Answer the following questions in the affirmative as in the example. Then repeat the correct sentence after the speaker gives it.*

Example: È molto grande la casa?
Sí, è una casona.

1. .... 3. ....

2. .... 4. ....

Example: È brutta la casa, vero?
Sí, è una casaccia.

1. .... 3. ....

2. .... 4. ....

D. *Create new sentences by substituting in the base sentence the words given.*

Example: Questa non è una casetta, è una casona.
terrazzina
Questa non è una terrazzina, è una terrazzona.

....

....

NAME ______________________ DATE ____________ CLASS ____________

UNIT 14

Part Two

G R A M M A T I C A

USES OF THE VERB *ANDARE*

A. *Create new sentences by substituting in the base sentence the subjects supplied.*

1. Example: Vanno sempre a scuola a piedi.
   tu
   Vai sempre a scuola a piedi.

   ....

   ....

2. Example: Non vado d'accordo con i miei amici.
   Giacomo
   Giacomo non va d'accordo con i suoi amici.

   ....

   ....

B. *Answer the following questions in the negative, using conjunctive pronouns. Then repeat the correct sentence after the speaker gives it.*

Example: Ha fame lei, vuole mangiare?
No, non le va di mangiare.

1. .... 3. .... 5. ....

2. .... 4. ....

LISTENING/COMPREHENSION

Listen to the following dialogue.

LE VACANZE

Laura e Gianna parlano di vacanze.

Laura: Appena arriva il bel tempo voglio andare in qualche isola.
Gianna: L'Italia è ricca di isole e isolette; e sono tutte bellissime.
Laura: Le isole hanno sempre qualcosa di speciale. Il mare mi piace tanto e starei sempre in acqua a nuotare come un pesce.
Gianna: Per me le vacanze non sono vacanze se non c'è aria e sole. Il mare, la campagna, la collina, la montagna vanno tutti bene: voglio vivere all'aria aperta.
Laura: Che cosa fai quando vai in campagna? Non ti annoi? Io mi annoio moltissimo in campagna.
Gianna: Io no, mi diverto. Vado a fare delle passeggiate nei boschi; vado in cerca di fragole, di funghi, di asparagi selvatici, oppure mi siedo all'ombra degli alberi e leggo. Gioco a tennis se c'è un campo da tennis e nuoto se c'è una piscina.
Laura: Hai mai fatto delle gite in bicicletta, andando alla ventura, con lo zaino sulle spalle?
Gianna: Sí, ho fatto qualche campeggio con la tenda e il sacco a pelo. Non ho mai avuto molta voglia di dormire per terra, però. Preferisco un vero letto, io.
Laura: Con chi vai in vacanza di solito?
Gianna: Con gli amici e tu?
Laura: Spesso con mia sorella. Andiamo in una casetta in riva al mare: c'è una bella spiaggia davanti e in fondo alla spiaggia ci sono degli scogli bellissimi. Per tutta l'estate non facciamo che fare il bagno e prendere il sole.
Gianna: Di chi è la casa?
Laura: La prendiamo in affitto. Comprare una casa sul mare costa troppo!

QUESTIONS

You will hear six questions about the dialogue you have just heard. Indicate the correct answer to each question by circling the letter before it. You will hear each question twice.

1. ....

   a. in Italia

   b. in un'isola

   c. al sole

2. ....

   a. aria e sole

   b. andare in un'isola bellissima

   c. che solo la montagna e la collina vanno bene

NAME ______________________________ DATE ____________ CLASS ___________

3. ....

a. nuotare come un pesce

b. fare delle passeggiate nei boschi

c. annoiarsi moltissimo

4. ....

a. in una piscina

b. quando va in cerca di fragole

c. sotto l'ombra degli alberi

5. ....

a. non ha voglia di dormire per terra

b. nei boschi non ha la tenda e il sacco a pelo

c. non le piace andare con lo zaino sulle spalle

6. ....

a. su una spiaggia con gli scogli

b. mentre si prende il sole sulla riva del mare

c. su una tranquilla strada di campagna con dei begli alberi

INTONATION AND SOUND DISCRIMINATION

A. *Repeat the following questions and answers after the speaker, keeping the question and statement intonation and pronouncing carefully.*

1. .... 3. .... 5. ....

2. .... 4. ....

B. *Repeat the following sentences after the speaker, keeping the speaker's intonation and pronouncing carefully.*

1. .... 4. .... 7. ....

2. .... 5. .... 8. ....

3. .... 6. ....

PRONUNCIATION

SOUND AND SPELLING OF /p/

A. *The consonant /p/ is pronounced as in English when it is in the middle of a word. At the beginning of a word, it is not aspirated as it is in English. Remember that all short vowels are pronounced distinctly, with the same pronunciation as long vowels.*

Repeat: pena polo Paolo può pongo
papavero peste pino tipo capí
apatico apolitico saputo aspro
simpatico spesso asparagi

B. *The spelling of /p/ is always* p *when the sound is uttered with low energy. A double* p *is used when the sound is uttered with high energy.*

Repeat the following pairs of words contrasting high and low energy /p/. Each pair will be repeated by the speaker so that you can check your pronunciation.

cape/cappe siepi/seppi papa/pappa pope/poppe
capello/cappello deputa/oppure tapino/tappino
la pena/appena Peppe/pepe scopa/coppa

Repeat the following sentences. Each of them will be read after you so that you can check your pronunciation.

prese la pipa e partí seppe che Paolo poteva
mio papà è apolitico il rapporto è appena finito
appartiene a un gruppo sportivo Peppe pesta il pepe
caspita che spocchia

C. *Write the following words. Each word will be repeated so that you can check your accuracy.*

____________________	____________________
____________________	____________________
____________________	____________________
____________________	____________________
____________________	____________________
____________________	____________________
____________________	____________________

NAME ______________________________ DATE ___________ CLASS ____________

D I C T A T I O N

Listen to the following sentences. Then write each sentence during the pause. The sentence will be repeated so that you can check your accuracy.

1. ____

   ____

2. ____

   ____

3. ____

   ____

4. ____

   ____

5. ____

   ____

NAME ______________________ DATE ____________ CLASS ____________

UNIT 15

Part One

D I A L O G U E

Listen to the following dialogue.

ANDANDO AL CINEMA

Giacomo, Laura, e Gianna chiacchierano camminando.

Laura: Fate presto che è tardi! Lo spettacolo sta per cominciare.
Gianna: Non c'è bisogno di correre. Sono le sette e mezzo e lo spettacolo non comincia che alle otto.
Giacomo: Abbiamo tempo, allora. Vado dal tabaccaio a comprare un pacchetto di sigarette.
Gianna: Vengo anch'io.

Now repeat each sentence after the speaker.

G R A M M A T I C A

I. THE *GERUNDIO*

A. *Create new sentences by substituting in the base sentence the* gerundio *form of the verbs supplied.*

1. Example: Uscendo, chiudi la porta!
andarsene
Andandotene, chiudi la porta!

....

....

2. Example: Stavo studiando.
mangiare
Stavo mangiando.

....

....

3. Example: Cosa fai, stai scrivendo?
leggere
Cosa fai, stai leggendo?

....

....

II. PROGRESSIVE PHRASES: *STARE* PLUS *GERUNDIO*

A. *Change the following sentences into the progressive, keeping the tense unchanged. Then repeat the correct sentence after the speaker gives it.*

Example: Fa freddo quest'anno.
Sta facendo freddo quest'anno.

1. .... 3. .... 5. ....

2. .... 4. ....

B. *Change the following sentences from the progressive into the tense of* stare *as in the example. Then repeat the correct sentence after the speaker gives it.*

Example: Stavate mangiando la cena.
Mangiavate la cena.

1. .... 3. .... 5. ....

2. .... 4. ....

C. *Change the following sentences by attaching the pronouns to the* gerundio. *Then repeat the correct sentence after the speaker gives it.*

Example: Glielo sto dicendo.
Sto dicendoglielo.

1. .... 3. .... 5. ....

2. .... 4. .... 6. ....

NAME ______________________________ DATE ____________ CLASS ____________

D. *Change the following sentences by detaching all pronouns from the* gerundio. *Then repeat the correct sentence after the speaker gives it.*

Example: Stava andandosene al cinema.
Se ne stava andando al cinema.

1. .... 3. .... 5. ....

2. .... 4. .... 6. ....

III. STARE + PER + INFINITIVE

A. *Change the following sentences: substitute* stare *plus* per *plus infinitive for the verb, keeping the tense unchanged. Then repeat the correct sentence after the speaker gives it.*

Example: Gli ospiti tornano da Milano.
Gli ospiti stanno per tornare da Milano.

1. .... 4. .... 7. ....

2. .... 5. .... 8. ....

3. .... 6. ....

IV. PER + INFINITIVE

A. *Change the following sentences by substituting* per *plus infinitive for* perché *plus clause. Then repeat the correct sentence after the speaker gives it.*

Example: Giacomo fuma perché vuole calmarsi i nervi.
Giacomo fuma per calmarsi i nervi.

1. .... 3. .... 5. ....

2. .... 4. .... 6. ....

V. USES OF PRIMA DI, INVECE DI, DOPO, SENZA

A. *Change the following sentences by substituting* prima di *plus infinitive for* poi *plus verb as in the example. Then repeat the correct sentence after the speaker gives it.*

Example: Prima scriverò una lettera, poi andrò a casa.
Scriverò una lettera prima di andare a casa.

1. .... 3. .... 5. ....

2. .... 4. ....

B. *Change the following sentences: substitute* invece di *plus infinitive for* non *plus verb as in the example. Then repeat the correct sentence after the speaker gives it.*

Example: Non vado a casa, preferisco scrivere una lettera.
Invece di andare a casa scrivo una lettera.

1. .... 3. .... 5. ....

2. .... 4. ....

C. *Change the following sentences: substitute* senza *plus infinitive for* ma non *plus verb as in the example. Then repeat the correct sentence after the speaker gives it.*

Example: Scriverò una lettera ma non glielo dirò.
Scriverò una lettera senza dirglielo.

1. .... 3. ....

2. .... 4. ....

D. *Answer the following questions using the future plus* dopo *plus the appropriate compound infinitive. Then repeat the correct sentence after the speaker gives it.*

Example: Quando vai a casa, scriverai una lettera?
Scriverò una lettera dopo essere andato a casa.

1. .... 3. .... 5. ....

2. .... 4. ....

NAME ________________ DATE ________ CLASS ________

UNIT 15

Part Two

ECCO + PRONOUNS

A. *Make new sentences from the following, using* ecco *plus pronouns as in the examples. Then repeat the correct sentence after the speaker gives it.*

Examples: Il pane è qui.
Eccolo.

Ti dò il pane.
Eccotelo.

1. ....
2. ....
3. ....
4. ....
5. ....
6. ....
7. ....
8. ....
9. ....

L I S T E N I N G / C O M P R E H E N S I O N

Listen to the following dialogue.

PIANI PER UNA SERATA FUORI CASA

Laura, Giacomo e Gianna fanno progetti per la sera.

Laura: *(bussando alla porta)* È permesso? La porta è aperta.
Gianna: Entra, entra, vi stavo aspettando. Dov'è Giacomo? Non è con te?
Laura: Sí, sta salendo le scale; l'ascensore non funziona. Che stai facendo?
Gianna: Sto scrivendo una lettera, ma sto per finire.
Laura: Ma che fai? Scrivi sempre? Anche ieri quando ti ho telefonato, stavi scrivendo.
Gianna: Ah sí? Non stavo mangiando? Di solito mangio mentre telefono.
Giacomo: Ciao! Siete pronte per uscire? Che volete fare: andare al cinema o a teatro?
Laura: Andiamo al cinema.

Gianna: C'è odore di fumo qui dentro?
Laura: Io non sento nessun odore.
Gianna: Se non avete freddo, apro la finestra per un minuto e poi la richiudo subito.
Laura: Fa' pure. Allora, a che spettacolo andiamo?
Giacomo: Andiamo a quello delle otto. Mangiamo dopo lo spettacolo, no?
Laura: Perché non andiamo a cena prima di andare al cinema? Io ho molta fame.
Gianna: No, no, è troppo presto per cenare e poi non c'è tempo se vogliamo andare alle otto.
Laura: Va bene. Però andiamo a un cinema di seconda visione. Io non ho soldi.
Gianna: Non ti preoccupare. Siamo tutti al verde. C'è un bel film al cinema qui all'angolo.
Giacomo: Che danno?
Gianna: Non mi ricordo come si chiama, ma è un film poliziesco di un regista famoso e con dei bravi attori.
Laura: Perfetto, andiamo allora.
Gianna: Laura, uscendo, chiudi la porta per piacere.

QUESTIONS

You will hear seven questions about the dialogue you have just heard. Indicate the correct answer to each question by circling the letter before it. You will hear each question twice.

1. ....
   a. entra, entra...
   b. vi stavo aspettando
   c. è permesso?

2. ....
   a. sta salendo con l'ascensore
   b. sta salendo le scale
   c. l'ascensore funziona

3. ....
   a. scrive una lettera
   b. sta mangiando
   c. sta telefonando

4. ....
   a. a teatro
   b. al cinema
   c. a fare una passeggiata

5. ....
   a. ha freddo
   b. la richiude subito
   c. dice che c'è odore di fumo

6. ....
   a. hanno molta fame
   b. vogliono andare allo spettacolo delle dieci
   c. non c'è tempo per cenare

7. ....
   a. c'è un bel film poliziesco
   b. hanno tutti abbastanza soldi
   c. vogliono andare a un cinema di prima visione

NAME ______________________ DATE ____________ CLASS ____________

INTONATION AND SOUND DISCRIMINATION

A. *Repeat the following positive and negative sentences after the speaker. Notice the subtle difference in intonation between positive and negative statements.*

1. ....
2. ....
3. ....
4. ....
5. ....
6. ....
7. ....

B. *Repeat the following questions after the speaker, pronouncing carefully and using question intonation.*

1. ....
2. ....
3. ....
4. ....
5. ....
6. ....
7. ....

PRONUNCIATION

SOUND AND SPELLING OF /l/

A. *The consonant /l/ is not pronounced as in English. The tip of your tongue should be placed right behind your teeth. /l/ in Italian is pronounced more forward in the mouth than in English, never in the throat.*

Repeat: lena Lina lana Laura luna
lodevole pala palpito parlare
palma palomba abulico paralume
malocchio malora sloggiato sleale

B. *The spelling of /l/ is always* l *when the sound is uttered with low energy. A double* l *is used when it is uttered with high energy. Remember that vowels are short before high-energy consonants and long before low-energy consonants. Remember too that short vowels are pronounced exactly like long vowels; only the length is different.*

Repeat the following pairs of words contrasting high and low energy /l/. Each pair will be repeated after you so that you can check your pronunciation.

pala/palla peli/pelli bolo/bollo Sila/Silla
malora/ma allora Elena/ellenico scolato/scollato
mole/molle sciali/scialli sul/sullo

Repeat the following phrases. Each of them will be read after you so that you can check your pronunciation.

l'ala dell'allodola — Elena è ellenica — allora è solo?

pallida luna — un malevolo pallore — un pallone bolide

il polline è pulito — si è slargato

C. *Write the following words. Each word will be repeated so that you can check your accuracy.*

____________________	____________________
____________________	____________________
____________________	____________________
____________________	____________________
____________________	____________________
____________________	____________________
____________________	____________________

D I C T A T I O N

Listen to the following sentences. Then write each sentence during the pause. Each sentence will be repeated so that you can check your accuracy.

1. ____

   ____

2. ____

   ____

3. ____

   ____

4. ____

   ____

5. ____

   ____

NAME ______________________ DATE __________ CLASS __________

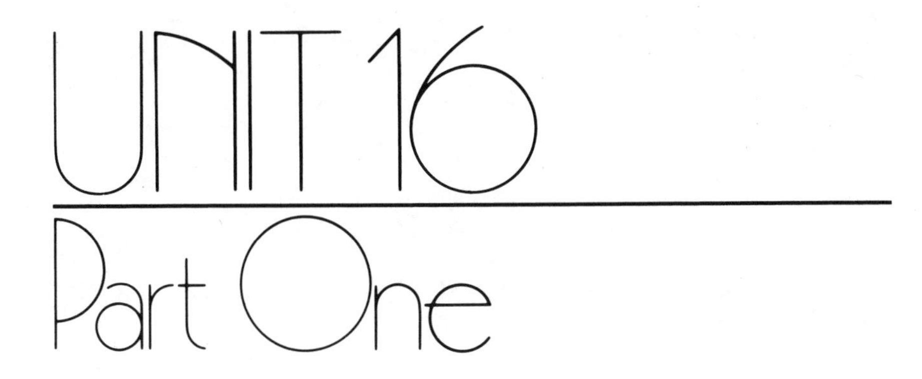

D I A L O G U E

Listen to the following dialogue.

IL GIORNALE RADIO

Giacomo e il suo amico Mario parlano del più e del meno.

Mario: Hai sentito il giornale radio stamattina?
Giacomo: Non ho ancora acceso la radio oggi. È stata spenta tutto il giorno. Perché?
Mario: Una banda di ladri ha derubato una banca.
Giacomo: Che hanno rubato?
Mario: Hanno preso soldi e gioielli di tutti i tipi: anelli d'oro, collane, spille, bracciali, catene per l'ammontare di molti milioni.

Now repeat each sentence after the speaker.

G R A M M A T I C A

I. THE CONDITIONAL

Create new sentences by substituting in the base sentence the subjects supplied.

1. Example: La zia guarderebbe sempre la televisione, ma non ha tempo.
   loro
   Guarderebbero sempre la televisione, ma non hanno tempo.

   ....

   ....

2. Example: Leggerei la mano a milioni di persone.
Giacomo
Giacomo leggerebbe la mano a milioni di persone.

....

....

3. Example: Partirei con loro, ma non sono stato invitato.
gli ospiti
Gli ospiti partirebbero con loro, ma non sono stati invitati.

....

....

B. *Change the following sentences from singular to plural. Then repeat the correct sentence after the speaker gives it.*

Example: Lo studente potrebbe comprare dei libri da Einaudi.
Gli studenti potrebberi comprare dei libri da Einaudi.

1. .... 3. .... 5. ....

2. .... 4. ....

C. *Answer the following questions in the conditional tense using the noun subjects supplied. Then repeat the correct sentence after the speaker gives it.*

Example: Che cosa ti serve?
un libro di storia
Mi servirebbe un libro di storia.

1. .... 3. .... 5. ....

2. .... 4. ....

D. *Answer the following questions affirmatively, using* piacere *in the conditional. Then repeat the correct sentence after the speaker gives it.*

Example: Andresti alla ventura?
Sì, mi piacerebbe andare alla ventura.

1. .... 3. .... 5. ....

2. .... 4. ....

NAME ______________________ DATE ____________ CLASS ____________

II. USES OF THE PREPOSITIONS *DA* AND *DI*

A. *Complete the following sentences using either* da *or* di *and making any necessary contractions. Then repeat the correct sentence during the second pause.*

Examples: 1. Quando ceno fuori vado _____ Alfredo.
Quando ceno fuori vado da Alfredo.

2. Una banda _____ ladri ha derubato la banca.
Una banda di ladri ha derubato la banca.

1. .... 3. .... 5. ....

2. .... 4. .... 6. ....

NAME ______________________ DATE ____________ CLASS ____________

UNIT 16

Part Two

G R A M M A T I C A

I. USES OF THE PREPOSITIONS *A* AND *DI* PLUS THE INFINITIVE AFTER VERBS SUCH AS *PROMETTERE, CONTINUARE, RICORDARE,* ETC.

A. *Complete the following sentences by inserting either* a *or* di *as in the examples. Then repeat the correct sentence during the second pause.*

Examples: Mi ricordo _____ scrivere a tuo padre.
Mi ricordo di scrivere a tuo padre.

Continuo _____ scrivere a tuo padre.
Continuo a scrivere a tuo padre.

1. ....
2. ....
3. ....
4. ....
5. ....
6. ....
7. ....
8. ....

II. RELATIVE PRONOUNS *CHE* AND *CUI*

A. *You will hear two sentences at a time. Use* che *to combine them into one. Then repeat the correct sentence after the speaker gives it.*

Example: Mio fratello ha scritto un libro. Il libro parla della sua vita.
Mio fratello ha scritto un libro che parla della sua vita.

1. ....
2. ....
3. ....
4. ....

Example: I ladri stanno scappando. I ladri hanno derubato la banca.
I ladri che hanno derubato la banca stanno scappando.

1. .... 3. ....

2. .... 4. ....

B. *You will hear two sentences at a time. Use* cui *to combine them into one. Then repeat the correct sentence during the second pause.*

Example: I ladri sono fuggiti. La macchina dei ladri è da corsa.
I ladri la cui macchina è da corsa, sono fuggiti.

1. .... 3. .... 5. ....

2. .... 4. ....

C. *Complete the following sentences with either* che *or* cui. *Then repeat the correct sentence after the speaker gives it.*

Examples: La macchina _____ compro è da corsa.
La macchina che compro è da corsa.

La macchina con _____ parto è una Fiat.
La macchina con cui parto è una Fiat.

1. .... 3. .... 5. ....

2. .... 4. .... 6. ....

LISTENING / COMPREHENSION

Listen to the following dialogue.

IL FRATELLO DI GIANNA

Gianna e Laura vanno alla libreria Einaudi.

Gianna: Mi accompagneresti alla libreria Einaudi?
Laura: Ci vengo volentieri. Anch'io devo comprare dei libri.
Gianna: Io non devo comprare libri, vorrei presentarti mio fratello.
Laura: Scusa sai? Ma che c'entra tuo fratello con la libreria?
Gianna: È una lunga storia. Questo è il fratello di cui ti ho parlato cento volte.
Laura: Qual è? Quello che ha deciso di scappare di casa a quindici anni e di cui non avete avuto notizie per dieci anni?
Gianna: Proprio lui. Ora ha scritto un libro la cui storia parla delle sue avventure fuori di casa.
Laura: Mi piacerebbe conoscere un tipo cosí straordinario. E il libro, da chi è stato pubblicato?
Gianna: Da Einaudi. È uscito qualche giorno fa e oggi c'è un ricevimento in suo onore.

NAME ________________________________ DATE ____________ CLASS ____________

Laura: Allora vale la pena scappare di casa quando riusciamo ad affermarci.
Gianna: Io lo invidio molto perché malgrado tutte le mie "proteste" non faccio che vivere una stupida vita da borghese.
Laura: Anche la mia vita è ben noiosa: studio e casa, casa e studio. Dovremmo proprio fare qualcosa di più emozionante.
Gianna: Cominciamo con fare il proposito di non evitare mai l'avventura e l'ignoto.
Laura: Benissimo e poi pensiamo a un motto da cui possiamo trarre ispirazione.
Gianna: Come ti sembra questo? "Coloro i cui pensieri, le cui azioni e i cui sentimenti mancano d'immaginazione, di senso d'umorismo, e di vitalità non meritano di essere nostri amici."
Laura: Va benissimo e l'accetto di tutto cuore. Impariamolo a memoria e promettiamo di ricordarcelo anche da vecchie.

QUESTIONS

You will hear eight questions about the dialogue you have just heard. Indicate the correct answer to each question by circling the letter before it. You will hear each question twice.

1. ....
   a. ad andare da suo fratello
   b. alla libreria Einaudi
   c. a leggere un libro

2. ....
   a. presentare suo fratello a Laura
   b. deve comprare dei libri
   c. vuole accompagnare Laura

3. ....
   a. ha raccontato una lunga storia
   b. è entrato nella libreria
   c. ha deciso di scappare di casa a quindici anni

4. ....
   a. delle notizie che non ha dato per dieci anni
   b. della casa che aveva a quindici anni
   c. delle sue avventure fuori di casa

5. ....
   a. dieci anni fa
   b. qualche giorno fa
   c. oggi

6. ....
   a. perché lei vive una stupida vita
   b. perché il fratello vive da borghese
   c. perché protesta molto

7. ....
   a. che la sua vita è divertente
   b. che la sua vita è noiosa
   c. che la sua vita è piena d'avventure

8. ....
   a. di mancare d'immaginazione
   b. di evitare il senso d'umorismo
   c. di non evitare mai l'avventura e l'ignoto

INTONATION AND SOUND DISCRIMINATION

A. *Listen to the following sentences using verbs in the conditional. Repeat each after the speaker, then circle the subject of the verb at right. You will hear each sentence twice.*

1.	io	tu	lei/lui	noi	voi	loro
2.	io	tu	lei/lui	noi	voi	loro
3.	io	tu	lei/lui	noi	voi	loro
4.	io	tu	lei/lui	noi	voi	loro
5.	io	tu	lei/lui	noi	voi	loro
6.	io	tu	lei/lui	noi	voi	loro
7.	io	tu	lei/lui	noi	voi	loro

B. *Listen to the following sentences in which either* di *or* da *is used. Repeat each after the speaker, then circle* di *or* da. *You will hear each sentence twice.*

1.	di	da	4.	di	da
2.	di	da	5.	di	da
3.	di	da	6.	di	da

PRONUNCIATION

SOUND AND SPELLING OF /m/

A. *The consonant* /m/ *is pronounced as in English. Remember to pronounce short vowels in unstressed syllables just like long vowels in stressed syllables, changing only the length.*

Repeat: male melo mulo molo Milo almeno
Romolo semina remano armeno fumano
fumo demone smanie smemorato

B. *The spelling of* /m/ *is always* m *when the sound is uttered with low energy. A double* m *is used when it is uttered with high energy.*

Repeat the following pairs of words contrasting high and low energy /m/. *Each pair will be repeated by the speaker so that you can check your pronunciation.*

NAME ______________________ DATE ____________ CLASS ____________

m'ama/mamma   dama/dammi   pomo/sommo

imitare/immettere   gema/gemma   doma/domma

emana/emma   coma/comma   fumo/fummo

schiuma/mummia   camino/cammino

Repeat the following phrases. Each of them will be repeated so that you can check your pronunciation.

la mamma ama Mimi   Mimma, fumalo   non amarmi di meno

dammi la mano   Amelia cammina con un lumino

è un uomo che cammina sul camino?   il lirismo smuove

C. *Write the following words. Each word will be repeated so that you can check your accuracy.*

______________________   ______________________

______________________   ______________________

______________________   ______________________

______________________   ______________________

______________________   ______________________

____

D I C T A T I O N

Listen to the following sentences. Then write each sentence during the pause. Each sentence will be repeated so that you can check your accuracy.

1. ____

____

2. ____

____

3. ____

____

4. ____

____

5. ____

____

NAME ________________ DATE ________ CLASS ________

UNIT 17

Part One

D I A L O G U E

Listen to the following dialogue.

UNA PERSONA CAMBIA

Gianna e Giacomo parlano di Laura.

Gianna: L'altro giorno ho parlato a lungo con Laura.
Giacomo: Di che cosa avete parlato?
Gianna: Mi diceva che quando era in America si sentiva molto americana. E ora invece, non si sente né italiana né americana.
Giacomo: Pensa forse che non si troverà bene quando ritornerà negli Stati Uniti?
Gianna: Oh no! Mi ha semplicemente spiegato che ora si sente più libera, più sicura.

Now repeat each sentence after the speaker.

G R A M M A T I C A

I. THE PAST ABSOLUTE

A. *Create new sentences by substituting in the base sentence the subjects supplied.*

1. Example: Un giorno partisti dalla fattoria.
   mio fratello
   Un giorno mio fratello partì dalla fattoria.

....

....

2. Example: Vendette la casa all'angolo.
l'albergatore
L'albergatore vendette la casa all'angolo.

....

....

3. Example: Gli regalai un orologio.
i suoi nonni
I suoi nonni gli regalarono un orologio.

....

....

4. Example: Le vacanze furono bellissime.
La vacanza
La vacanza fu bellissima.

....

....

5. Example: Ebbe una brutta giornata.
lo psichiatra
Lo psichiatra ebbe una brutta giornata.

....

....

B. *Change the following sentences from the compound past into the past absolute. Then repeat the correct sentence after the speaker gives it.*

Example: Ho capito tutto.
Capii tutto.

1. .... 5. ....

2. .... 6. ....

3. .... 7. ....

4. .... 8. ....

NAME ______________________ DATE __________ CLASS __________

II. INDEFINITE *QUALCHE* AND *ALCUNO*

A. *In the following sentences replace the quantifiers and the indefinite articles with* qualche. *Then repeat the correct sentence after the speaker gives it.*

Example: Feci dei regali alla bambina.
Feci qualche regalo alla bambina.

1. ....
2. ....
3. ....
4. ....

B. *Change the following sentences: replace the partitives with* alcuni *or* alcune *as in the example. Then repeat the correct sentence after the speaker gives it.*

Example: Voglio dei giornali.
Voglio alcuni giornali.

1. ....
2. ....
3. ....
4. ....
5. ....
6. ....

C. *In the following sentences replace the direct object with* ne *and* alcuni *or* alcune. *Then repeat the correct sentence after the speaker gives it.*

Example: Voglio dei libri.
Ne voglio alcuni.

1. ....
2. ....
3. ....
4. ....

III. INDIRECT DISCOURSE: DEPENDENT CLAUSES

A. *Change the following sentences by connecting the two clauses as in the examples. Then repeat the correct sentence after the speaker gives it.*

Example: Laura dice: "Mi piace la musica folk."
Laura dice che le piace la musica folk.

1. ....
2. ....
3. ....
4. ....

Example: Mia madre gli ha chiesto: "Ha avuto fortuna?"
Mia madre gli ha chiesto se aveva avuto fortuna.

1. .... 3. .... 5. ....

2. .... 4. ....

B. *Change the following sentences: change the command from direct to indirect using* di *plus infinitive. Then repeat the correct sentence after the second pause.*

Example: Il professore disse: imparate la lezione!
Il professore disse di imparare la lezione.

1. .... 3. .... 5. ....

2. .... 4. .... 6. ....

NAME ______________________ DATE ____________ CLASS ____________

UNIT 17

Part Two

G R A M M A T I C A

I. ADJECTIVE AND PRONOUN *TUTTO*

A. *Expand the following sentences by adding the correct form of* tutto *before the noun. Then repeat the correct sentence after the speaker gives it.*

Example: I ladri rubano.
Tutti i ladri rubano.

1. ....
2. ....
3. ....
4. ....
5. ....
6. ....
7. ....

B. *Answer the following questions in the affirmative using the correct form of* tutto. *Then repeat the correct sentence after the speaker gives it.*

Example: Hai visto il film?
Sí, l'ho visto tutto.

1. ....
2. ....
3. ....
4. ....
5. ....

L I S T E N I N G / C O M P R E H E N S I O N

Listen to the following dialogue.

LA STORIA DI BRUNO

Bruno parla con Laura delle sue avventure.

Laura: Cosí un giorno partisti dalla fattoria del signor Mancini.
Bruno: Sí, avvenne all'improvviso. Avevo passato dei begli anni dai Mancini, avevo imparato molte cose nuove...
Laura: Vivevi naturalmente in modo diverso.
Bruno: Proprio cosí. I valori, le preoccupazioni della gente di campagna non sono quelli della gente di città. Un giorno però mi resi conto che volevo cambiar vita e tornare in città.
Laura: Parlasti di queste cose con il signor Mancini?
Bruno: Oh sí. Gli parlai francamente. Il signor Mancini era contadino, forse ignorante, ma era una persona estremamente intelligente e sensibile.
Laura: E che ti disse?
Bruno: Che gli dispiaceva molto vedermi partire, ma che capiva. Aggiunse che mi avrebbe sempre voluto bene come a un figlio.
Laura: Che persona straordinaria!
Bruno: Cosí il giorno dopo riempii lo zaino della mia poca roba, feci qualche regalo alla famiglia e...
Laura: Che cosa regalasti al signor Mancini?
Bruno: Gli regalai un orologio.
Laura: Sono sicura che ne fu molto contento.
Bruno: Oh sí, si commosse! Ebbe un momento di esitazione poi lo prese e mi abbracciò.
Laura: Andasti alla stazione da solo?
Bruno: No, il signor Mancini promise che mi ci avrebbe accompagnato lui. La mattina facemmo una lunga colazione. Ridemmo e piangemmo ricordando tutto il tempo passato insieme...
Laura: Cosí faceste tardi e perdeste il treno delle sette e mezzo.
Bruno: Sí, ma il signor Mancini mi accompagnò a quello seguente.
Laura: Non ti dispiacque partire e lasciare la vita dura del contadino?
Bruno: Molto, ma fu una decisione che non ho mai rimpianto.

QUESTIONS

You will hear seven questions about the dialogue you have just heard. Indicate the correct answer to each question by circling the letter before it. You will hear each question twice.

1. ....

a. aveva passato dei begli anni

b. aveva imparato molte cose

c. all'improvviso

NAME ______________________________ DATE ____________ CLASS ___________

2. ....

a. voleva tornare in città

b. viveva in modo diverso

c. i valori della gente di campagna erano diventati i suoi

3. ....

a. una persona intelligente e sensibile

b. una persona che non capiva niente

c. un uomo che parlava francamente

4. ....

a. era suo figlio

b. aveva imparato a volergli bene

c. partiva per la città

5. ....

a. per sapere l'ora

b. per guardare l'orologio

c. per trasportare della roba

6. ....

a. della roba che aveva Bruno

b. dell'orologio che gli regalò Bruno

c. della sua vita dura

7. ....

a. il signor Mancini accompagnò Bruno

b. fecero una lunga colazione

c. gli dispiaceva partire

INTONATION AND SOUND DISCRIMINATION

A. *You will hear six sentences on tape. After listening to each, indicate the one you heard by circling the letter before it. You will hear each sentence twice.*

1. a. Aspetta la signora Spina.
   b. Ascolta la signora Spina.

2. a. Non aprire, fa freddo.
   a. In aprile, non fa freddo.

3. a. Dov'è la pasta?
   b. Dov'è la posta?

4. a. Il loro pasto.
   b. Il loro posto.

5. a. Vedono la macchina.
   b. Vendono la macchina.

6. a. È andato a fare due passi.
   b. È andato a prendere due sassi.

B. *Listen to the following sentences in which someone is being spoken or thought of. Repeat each after the speaker, then circle the subject of the second verb. You will hear each sentence twice.*

1.	io	tu	lei/lui	noi	voi	loro
2.	io	tu	lei/lui	noi	voi	loro
3.	io	tu	lei/lui	noi	voi	loro
4.	io	tu	lei/lui	noi	voi	loro
5.	io	tu	lei/lui	noi	voi	loro
6.	io	tu	lei/lui	noi	voi	loro

C. *Listen to the following sentences in which forms of* tutto *are used. Repeat each after the speaker, then circle the noun at right with which it agrees. You will hear each sentence twice.*

1.	gli spaghetti	la carne
2.	il caffè	la limonata
3.	i giornali	le riviste
4.	i ragazzi	le ragazze
5.	gli studenti	le studentesse

P R O N U N C I A T I O N

SOUND AND SPELLING OF /n/

A. *The consonant /n/ is pronounced as in English in most cases. Before /k/ and /g/, /n/ is articulated in the back of the mouth, but it is not nasal as in English. Remember to pronounce short vowels just like long vowels, varying only the length.*

Repeat: nano nino numero nono almeno
temono ancora angora anche fianchi
angheria mirano canguro anonimo
snervato snido

B. *The spelling of /n/ is always* n *when the sound is uttered with low energy. A double* n *is used when it is uttered with high energy.*

Repeat the following pairs of words contrasting high and low energy /n/. Each word will be repeated by the speaker so that you can check your pronunciation.

nana/nanna nono/nonno pena/penna

canone/cannone sano/sanno Nino/inno

Pina/pinna anello/cannello pane/panne

penati/pennati

Repeat the following sentences. Each will be read after you so that you can check your accuracy.

Nina canta la ninna nanna la nonna non è Anna

sanno dov'è il cannone nano è l'anello di nonna?

ninnalo tu invece del nonno è uno snob snaturato

C. *Write the following words. Each word will be repeated so that you can check your accuracy.*

______________ ______________

______________ ______________

______________ ______________

______________ ______________

______________ ______________

______________ ______________

______________ ______________

D I C T A T I O N

Listen to the following sentences. Then write each sentence during the pause. Each sentence will be repeated so that you can check your accuracy.

1. ______________________________________

____

2. ______________________________________

____

3. ____

____

4. ____

____

5. ____

____

NAME ______________________ DATE __________ CLASS __________

UNIT 18 Part One

D I A L O G U E

Listen to the following dialogue.

DIFFERENZA D'OPINIONI

Giacomo e sua madre parlano dell'atteggiamento dei giovani e dei vecchi riguardo al divorzio.

Giacomo: Sai mamma? Ho appena ricevuto una telefonata da Luisa Marini.
Madre: Ah sí? Che fa? Come sta? Spero che stia bene.
Giacomo: Si sposa con un medico la settimana prossima.
Madre: Ma come, cosí presto? Si è appena divorziata!
Giacomo: Mamma! Il primo marito non è mica morto! Voglio che tu capisca che il divorzio non è come morire. I tempi sono cambiati. Ti assicuro che a volte ho l'impressione che tu viva nel mondo della luna.

Now repeat each sentence after the speaker.

G R A M M A T I C A

I. INDEFINITE *QUALUNQUE, QUALSIASI, QUALCUNO*

A. *Change the following sentences from the affirmative to the negative. Then repeat the correct sentence after the speaker gives it.*

Example: Qualunque persona cambia.
Nessuna persona cambia.

1. .... 3. .... 5. ....

2. .... 4. .... 6. ....

B. *Answer the following questions in the affirmative using* qualcuno. *Then repeat the correct sentence after the speaker gives it.*

Example: Vuoi delle sigarette?
Sí, ne voglio qualcuna.

1. .... 3. .... 5. ....

2. .... 4. ....

C. *Change the following sentences from the negative to the affirmative. Then repeat the correct sentence after the speaker gives it.*

Example: Non ho parlato a nessuno.
Ho parlato a qualcuno.

1. .... 3. .... 5. ....

2. .... 4. ....

II. THE PRESENT SUBJUNCTIVE

A. *Create new sentences by substituting in the base sentence the verbs supplied.*

1. Example: Mi sembra che parli.
discutere
Mi sembra che discuta.

....

....

2. Example: Bisogna che cambino.
discutere
Bisogna che discutano.

....

....

3. Example: Spera che partiate
leggere
Spera che leggiate.

....

....

NAME ________________________________ DATE ____________ CLASS ____________

B. *Create new subordinate clauses by substituting in the base sentence the subjects supplied.*

1. Example: Laura crede che gli ospiti arrivino domani.
   l'ospite
   Laura crede che l'ospite arrivi domani.

....

....

2. Example: Non è possibile che tu non capisca.
   loro
   Non è possibile che non capiscano.

....

....

C. *Restate the following sentences: use the word supplied plus the present subjunctive and omit* ma. *Then repeat the correct sentence after the speaker gives it.*

Example: Sto a casa ma non guardo la televisione.
benché
Benché stia a casa, non guardo le televisione.

1. ....   3. ....   5. ....

2. ....   4. ....

III. MORE USES OF THE SUBJUNCTIVE

A. *Create new subordinate clauses by substituting in the base sentence the words given.*

Example: Preferisco qualcuno che dica la verità.
essere contento
Preferisco qualcuno che sia contento.

....

....

NAME ________________________ DATE ____________ CLASS ____________

UNIT 18

Part Two

GRAMMATICA

USES OF THE SUBJUNCTIVE—PRESENT SUBJUNCTIVE REVIEW

A. *Create new sentences by substituting in the base sentence the verbs supplied.*

1. Example: Voglio che tu sappia
   andare
   Voglio che tu vada.

   ....

   ....

2. Example: Può darsi che ci pensi molto.
   parlarne
   Può darsi che ne parli molto.

   ....

   ....

3. Example: Non so che cosa possa comprare.
   dovere scrivere
   Non so che cosa debba scrivere.

   ....

   ....

B. *Change the following sentences into superlative statements, using the words supplied and the subjunctive. Then repeat the correct sentence after the speaker gives it.*

Example: Questa è una bella casa.
ho visto
Questa è la casa più bella che abbia visto.

1. .... 3. .... 5. ....

2. .... 4. ....

C. *You will hear two sentences at a time. Make them into one using* che *plus subjunctive. Then repeat the correct sentence after the speaker gives it.*

Example: Non credo.
Gli ospiti tornano domani.
Non credo che gli ospiti tornino domani.

1. .... 3. .... 5. ....

2. .... 4. .... 6. ....

L I S T E N I N G / C O M P R E H E N S I O N

Listen to the following dialogue.

IDEE SUL MATRIMONIO

Gianna e Laura parlano del secondo matrimonio di Luisa.

Gianna: Non capisco perché Luisa voglia risposarsi.
Laura: Perché no? Se vuole bene al suo uomo.
Gianna: Ma che seccatura sposarsi una seconda volta!
Laura: Per qualcuno forse, ma si dice che il secondo matrimonio sia sempre migliore del primo, perché si sa quello che si fa.
Gianna: Comunque sia; credo che io preferirei non risposarmi.
Laura: Negli affari personali, qualsiasi comportamento per me va bene.
Gianna: Tu hai voglia di sposarti?
Laura: No, qualche anno fa ne avevo voglia. Ora non ne ho nessuna, malgrado mi senta un po' sola a volte. Mi basta avere un ragazzo che mi voglia bene.
Gianna: Che tipo di uomo ti piace?
Laura: Qualunque uomo per me va bene, purché sia bello, alto, magro, intelligente, ricco, pieno d'immaginazione, di fascino, di senso d'umorismo, gentile, interessante, colto, ben educato, un po' romantico e divertente.
Gianna: Con gli occhi neri, il naso dritto, eccetera. Ho capito, ti piace uno di quegli uomini che si trovano dappertutto. Insomma un uomo qualsiasi!

NAME ______________________ DATE ____________ CLASS ____________

Laura: Scusa sai, ma dato che nella mia fantasia posso scegliere, scelgo l'uomo perfetto, senza difetti.

Gianna: Ma siccome le persone perfette non esistono, è meglio essere un po' più realistici.

Laura: E infatti sono contenta del ragazzo di cui sono innamorata benché non sia perfetto.

QUESTIONS

You will hear six questions about the dialogue you have just heard. Indicate the correct answer to each question by circling the letter before it. You will hear each question twice.

1. ....

a. è una seccatura

b. è il secondo matrimonio

c. vuole bene al suo uomo

2. ....

a. perché si sa quello che si fa

b. qualcuno si sposa

c. forse perché ci si sposa una seconda volta

3. ....

a. sí, perché si sente sola

b. no, malgrado a volte si senta sola

c. qualche anno fa non ne aveva voglia

4. ....

a. né alto né intelligente

b. qualunque uomo va bene, purché non sia romantico

c. deve avere molte qualità

5. ....

a. perché sceglie nella sua fantasia

b. perché si trova dappertutto

c. perché ne è innamorata

6. ....

a. essere romantici

b. essere realistici

c. non pensare troppo al futuro

INTONATION AND SOUND DISCRIMINATION

A. *Listen to the following sentences in which either* qualunque *or* qualcuno *is used. Repeat the sentence after the speaker, then circle at right the word you hear. You will hear each sentence twice.*

1.	qualunque	qualcuno
2.	qualunque	qualcuno
3.	qualunque	qualcuno
4.	qualunque	qualcuno
5.	qualunque	qualcuno
6.	qualunque	qualcuno

B. *Listen to the following sentences in which the present subjunctive of either* essere *or* stare *is used. Repeat the sentence after the speaker, then circle at right the verb you hear. You will hear each sentence twice.*

1.	essere	stare
2.	essere	stare
3.	essere	stare
4.	essere	stare
5.	essere	stare
6.	essere	stare

PRONUNCIATION

SOUND AND SPELLING OF /d/

A. *The Italian consonant* /d/ *is pronounced differently from the English* d *in that the tip of the tongue is placed more forward in the mouth. The tip of the tongue is spread and gently touches the edge of the upper teeth.* s *before* d *is pronounced* /z/. *Remember to pronounce all short vowels in unstressed syllables distinctly, with the same pronunciation as long vowels in stressed syllables.*

NAME ______________________ DATE __________ CLASS __________

Repeat: do da di diamo dello dammelo

duro lardo sarda cardine sardine

ledono fidano andremo adeguato disdice

B. *The spelling of* /d/ *is always* d *when the sound is uttered with low energy. A double* d *is used when it is uttered with high energy.*

Repeat the following pairs of words contrasting high and low energy /d/. *Each word will be repeated by the speaker so that you can check your pronunciation.*

grida/ridda idiota/Iddio adone/addome

radice/addice sudi/suddito cado/addoloro

Adele/addette pedata/freddata

Repeat the following sentences. Each of the sentences will be read after you so that you can check your pronunciation.

si sdegna Adele ha freddo un grido non si addice

è un suddito idiota no si fidano dell'addetto

addio al dolore odia le rondini?

C. *Write the following words. Each word will be repeated so that you can check your accuracy.*

______________________ ______________________

______________________ ______________________

______________________ ______________________

______________________ ______________________

______________________ ______________________

____

D I C T A T I O N

Listen to the following sentences. Then write each sentence during the pause. Each sentence will be repeated so that you can check your accuracy.

1. ____

   ____

2. ____

   ____

3. ____

   ____

4. ____

   ____

5. ____

   ____

NAME ________________________ DATE ____________ CLASS ____________

DIALOGUE

Listen to the following dialogue.

UN VECCHIO AMICO

Pietro, un vecchio amico di Laura che vive in Sicilia, la va a prendere alla stazione di Catania.

Pietro: Ciao, sono proprio contento che sia riuscita a venire.
Laura: Ho avuto tanto da fare! Alla fine ho deciso che né l'università né lo studio mi avrebbero impedito di venire.
Pietro: Hai fatto bene.

Pietro: Quanto tempo è che non ci vediamo?
Laura: Non ci vediamo da due anni e mezzo, no? Che fai ora?
Pietro: Lavoro in una banca.

Now repeat each sentence after the speaker.

GRAMMATICA

I. THE PAST SUBJUNCTIVE

A. *Create new sentences by substituting in the base sentence the subjects given.*

1. Example: Magari i bambini stessero a casa!
   la nonna
   Magari la nonna stesse a casa!

....

....

2. Example: Vorrei che tu fossi qui.
voi
Vorrei che voi foste qui.

....

....

3. Example: Pensavo che Giacomo le dicesse tutto.
gli amici
Pensavo che gli amici le dicessero tutto.

....

....

4. Example: Mi piacerebbe che gli amici mi dessero ragione.
il mio amico
Mi piacerebbe che il mio amico mi desse ragione.

....

....

B. *Change the following sentences from the present to the imperfect, making all necessary changes. Then repeat the correct sentence after the speaker gives it.*

Example: Voglio che rimanga qui.
Volevo che rimanesse qui.

1. .... 3. .... 5. ....

2. .... 4. ....

C. *You will hear two sentences at a time. Combine them into one using* che *and the words supplied. Then repeat the correct sentence after the speaker gives it.*

Example: Facevo l'operaio.
Era necessario.
Era necessario che facessi l'operaio.

1. .... 3. .... 5. ....

2. .... 4. ....

NAME ______________________ DATE ____________ CLASS ____________

D. *Change the following sentences into statements of doubt using the phrases supplied and* se. *Then repeat the correct sentence after the speaker gives it.*

Example: Era andato a casa.
non sapevo
No sapevo se fosse andato a casa.

1. .... 3. .... 5. ....

2. .... 4. ....

II. SPECIAL CONJUNCTIONS: *NÉ...NÉ, SIA...CHE, O...O*

A. *Change the following sentences from negative to affirmative. Then repeat the correct sentence after the speaker gives it.*

Example: Né lo zio né la zia sono usciti ieri.
Lo zio e la zia sono usciti ieri.

1. .... 3. .... 5. ....

2. .... 4. ....

B. *Change the following sentences from negative to affirmative using* sia...che. *Then repeat the correct sentence after the speaker gives it.*

Example: Né lo zio né la zia sono usciti ieri.
Sia lo zio che la zia sono usciti ieri.

1. .... 3. .... 5. ....

2. .... 4. ....

C. *In the following sentences replace the conjunction* e *with* o...o. *Then repeat the correct sentence after the speaker gives it.*

Example: L'aereo e il treno vanno in Sicilia.
O l'aereo o il treno vanno in Sicilia.

1. .... 3. .... 5. ....

2. .... 4. ....

NAME ____________________ DATE __________ CLASS __________

UNIT 19

Part Two

III. TIME EXPRESSIONS

A. *In the following sentences replace the time expressions. Then put the verb into the compound past. Then repeat the correct sentence after the speaker gives it.*

Example: Laura starà a casa un'oretta.
due ore
Laura starà a casa due ore.
Laura è stata a casa due ore.

1. .... 3. .... 5. ....

2. .... 4. ....

L I S T E N I N G / C O M P R E H E N S I O N

Listen to the following dialogue.

VIAGGIO IN SICILIA

Laura va in un'agenzia di viaggi perché ha intenzione di fare un viaggio in Sicilia.

Laura: Vorrei andare a Catania. Qual è il modo migliore per andarci? L'aereo, il treno o la macchina?

Agente: Dipende da come preferisce viaggiare. Vuole che le prenoti anche una stanza in albergo?

Laura: No, vado ospite da alcuni amici, ma non vorrei che si preoccupassero troppo per me. Per questo ho pensato di prendere una macchina in affitto.

Agente: Se io fossi in Lei e dovessi viaggiare da solo, un viaggio così lungo non lo farei mai in macchina.

Laura: Se avessi la macchina sarei più libera. Ho una ventina di giorni a disposizione e potrei visitare i templi greci e le rovine romane di tutta la Sicilia senza disturbare i miei amici.

Agente: La macchina è molto cara e le si può rompere per la strada. Perché non va in treno o in aereo fino a Catania? Potrebbe sempre affittare una macchina sul luogo...a meno che non gliela prestino i suoi amici.

Laura: Ottima idea. Se non ne avessero bisogno mentre io sono loro ospite, me la potrebbero prestare e non spenderei una lira.

Agente: Allora, vuole un biglietto di seconda classe sul rapido?

Laura: Bene, allora mi dia un biglietto di seconda sul rapido. Me lo faccia d'andata e ritorno, per favore.

Agente: Per l'andata e ritorno c'è anche lo sconto se resta almeno una settimana. Ecco a Lei, grazie e buon viaggio.

Laura: Grazie.

QUESTIONS

You will hear eight questions about the dialogue you have just heard. Indicate the correct answer to each question by circling the letter before it. You will hear each question twice.

1. ....
   a. in aereo
   b. in treno
   c. in un'agenzia di viaggi

2. ....
   a. preferisce viaggiare
   b. va ospite di amici
   c. ha una stanza a Catania

3. ....
   a. si è più liberi
   b. la macchina si può rompere
   c. si può prendere una macchina in affitto

4. ....
   a. quasi tre settimane
   b. quindici giorni
   c. un mese

5. ....
   a. andare in treno
   b. affittare una macchina
   c. comprare una macchina

6. ....
   a. di prendere un biglietto di andata
   b. di andare in prima classe
   c. di prendere un biglietto di seconda sul rapido

7. ....
   a. un treno che va veloce
   b. un treno che va piano
   c. una treno che è più veloce di un aereo

8. ....
   a. paga una cosa di più
   b. che prende un biglietto di andata e ritorno
   c. che paga una cosa di meno

NAME ______________________ DATE ____________ CLASS ____________

I N T O N A T I O N A N D S O U N D D I S C R I M I N A T I O N

A. *Repeat after the speaker the following questions beginning with* quanto, *then tell whether they are in formal or informal address by circling* F *if formal,* I *if informal. You will hear each question twice.*

1. .... F I
2. .... F I
3. .... F I
4. .... F I
5. .... F I

B. *Sound discrimination. You will hear six sentences on tape. After listening to each, indicate the one you heard by circling the letter before it. You will hear each sentence twice.*

1. a. Vado al mercato.
   b. Vedo il mercato.
2. a. Prendiamo il gettone.
   b. Perdiamo il gettone.
3. a. Per chi lavorano loro?
   b. Perché lavorano loro?
4. a. Comprano tutto al mercato.
   b. Comprano tutto a buon mercato.
5. a. Non chiudeva mai niente.
   a. Non chiedeva mai niente.
6. a. Il nostro appuntamente.
   b. Il nostro appartamento.

P R O N U N C I A T I O N

SOUND AND SPELLING OF /t/

A. *The consonant /t/ is not pronounced as in English. The tongue is placed more forward in the mouth. The tip of the tongue is spread and gently touches the edge of the upper front teeth.*

Repeat: tino tana telo tubo tono
arto tavolo atono altalena Atene
mutila ruota futile latitudine astio
maestro

B. *The spelling of /t/ is always* t *when the sound is uttered with low energy. A double* t *is used when the sound is uttered with high energy. Long vowels precede low energy /t/; short vowels precede high energy /t/. Remember to pronounce all short vowels in unstressed syllables distinctly, with the same pronunciation as long vowels in stressed syllables.*

Repeat the following pairs of words contrasting low and high energy /t/. Each pair of words will be repeated so that you can check your pronunciation.

tuta/tutta meta/metta rito/ritto

patina/pattina fato/fatto malato/mulatto

ruta/rutta Rota/rotta otite/ottica

Repeat the following sentences. Each sentence will be read after you so that you can check your pronunciation.

ha tutta la tuta rotta i pattini di Pietro hanno una patina cristallina Ottavio e Italo è mosto misto se hai l'otite non ti serve un ottico ne metta la metà sul tavolo e l'altra sul letto

C. *Write the following words. Each word will be repeated so that you can check your accuracy.*

______________________ ______________________

______________________ ______________________

______________________ ______________________

______________________ ______________________

______________________ ______________________

______________________ ______________________

______________________ ______________________

____

NAME ______________________ DATE ____________ CLASS ____________

DICTATION

Listen to the following sentences. Then write each sentence during the pause. Each sentence will be repeated so that you can check your accuracy.

1. ____

____

2. ____

____

3. ____

____

4. ____

____

5. ____

____

NAME ______________________ DATE __________ CLASS __________

UNIT 20

Part One

D I A L O G U E

Listen to the following dialogue.

IN BANCA

Giacomo va in banca, si avvicina al banco e parla con un impiegato.

Giacomo: Dovrei riscuotere questo assegno che non è intestato a me...
Impiegato: Mi faccia vedere. Ma l'assegno non è neanche girato.
Giacomo: Già, questo è il problema. L'assegno è arrivato quando lui era già partito. Io ho un conto corrente e un libretto di risparmio in questa banca. Inoltre, il cassiere mi conosce personalmente.
Impiegato: Capisco, ma io non posso farci niente. Non sta a me darLe l'autorizzazione. Per riscuotere questo assegno, Le serve la firma dell'intestatario, o almeno una delega.

Now repeat each sentence after the speaker.

G R A M M A T I C A

I. *FARE* AND *LASCIARE* AS CAUSATIVE VERBS

A. *Change the following sentences by inserting the verb forms supplied as in the example. Then repeat the correct sentence after the speaker gives it.*

Example: I miei amici vanno a casa.
faccio
Faccio andare i miei amici a casa.

1. .... 3. .... 5. ....

2. .... 4. .... 6. ....

B. *Change the following sentences by inserting the verbs supplied as in the examples and keeping the subject the same. Then repeat the correct sentence after the speaker gives it.*

Examples: Cucinerà gli spaghetti per tutti.
fare
Farà cucinare gli spaghetti per tutti.

Cucino gli spaghetti per tutti.
lasciare
Lascio cucinare gli spaghetti per tutti.

1. .... 3. .... 5. ....

2. .... 4. .... 6. ....

C. *Change the following sentences: substitute the correct pronoun for the object of the infinitive. Then repeat the correct sentence after the speaker gives it.*

Example: Faccio leggere il libro alla studentessa.
Lo faccio leggere alla studentessa.

1. .... 3. ....

2. .... 4. ....

Example: Ha fatto studiare la lezione allo studente.
L'ha fatta studiare allo studente.

1. .... 3. ....

2. .... 4. ....

D. *In the following sentences substitute the correct pronouns for both direct and indirect object. Then repeat the correct sentence after the speaker gives it.*

Example: Faccio leggere il libro alle studentesse.
Glielo faccio leggere.

1. .... 3. .... 5. ....

2. .... 4. ....

NAME ________________ DATE ________ CLASS ________

E. *Change the following statements into formal commands, substituting the correct pronoun for any direct object. Then repeat the correct sentence after the speaker gives it.*

Examples: Si fa portare il caffè.
Se lo faccia portare!

Mi lascia vendere la casa.
Me la lasci vendere!

1. .... 3. .... 5. ....

2. .... 4. .... 6. ....

II. MORE ABOUT ADVERBS

A. *Change the following sentences from negative to affirmative, substituting* sempre *for* non...mai. *Then repeat the correct sentence after the speaker gives it.*

Example: Non leggo mai i giornali.
Leggo sempre i giornali.

1. .... 3. .... 5. ....

2. .... 4. ....

B. *Create new sentences by substituting in the base sentence the adverbs given.*

1. Example: Aspetta un momento!
qui
Aspetta qui!

....

....

2. Example: Non mangiare adesso!
qui
Non mangiare qui!

....

....

C. *Change the following sentences by using the opposite of the adverb you hear. Then repeat the correct sentence after the speaker gives it.*

Example: Può aspettarmi qui?
Può aspettarmi lì?

1. .... 3. .... 5. ....

2. .... 4. .... 6. ....

NAME ______________________ DATE ____________ CLASS ____________

UNIT 20

Part Two

USES OF *STARE*

A. *Answer the following questions as in the example. Then repeat the correct sentence after the speaker gives it.*

Example: Come ti sta il vestito?
Questo vestito non mi sta bene.

1. .... 3. ....

2. .... 4. ....

B. *Change the following sentences by substituting* stare *for* essere. *Then use conjunctive pronouns in place of all disjunctive pronouns. Then repeat the correct sentence after the speaker gives it.*

Example: I vestiti che ho comprato sono larghi per me.
I vestiti che ho comprato mi stanno larghi.

1. .... 3. .... 5. ....

2. .... 4. ....

C. *Change the following sentences by substituting impersonal* stare *for all forms of* dovere. *Then repeat the correct sentence after the speaker gives it.*

Example: I bambini devono giocare.
Sta ai bambini giocare.

1. .... 3. .... 5. ....

2. .... 4. ....

L I S T E N I N G / C O M P R E H E N S I O N

Listen to the following dialogue.

IL DIRETTORE DI BANCA

Giacomo va a parlare con il direttore della banca.

Direttore: Prego si accomodi!
Giacomo: Grazie. Avrei bisogno del Suo aiuto.
Direttore: Scusi, ma Lei non è il figlio del signor Fini?
Giacomo: Sí, ma come fa a saperlo?
Direttore: Assomiglia molto a Suo padre e Suo padre mi ha parlato di Lei.
Giacomo: Già, ci assomigliamo molto. Me lo dicono tutti.
Direttore: Mi dica cosa La porta qui.
Giacomo: Ho questo assegno che non è intestato a me e non mi sono fatto girare...
Direttore: Se non La conoscessi, non potrei fare niente per Lei. Le regole della banca sono molto severe per chi non è conosciuto. Ma dato che conosco bene Suo padre, sarò indulgente con Lei. Posso fidarmi di Lei, no?
Giacomo: Naturalmente! Vuol dire che mi fa riscuotere l'assegno?
Direttore: Sí, glielo faccio riscuotere subito, però mi deve portare una delega al piú presto.
Giacomo: Cioè...?
Direttore: Si deve far fare una delega dal suo amico.
Giacomo: In altre parole, mi devo far scrivere una lettera autorizzandomi a riscuotere l'assegno?
Direttore: Esattamente, poi la porta a me o all'impiegato. Mi firmi ora questa dichiarazione in cui mi promette di farmi avere la delega.
Giacomo: Ecco fatto. La ringrazio infinitamente di essersi fidato di me.

QUESTIONS

You will hear eight questions about the dialogue you have just heard. Indicate the correct answer to each question by circling the letter before it. You will hear each question twice.

1. ....

a. grazie, non ne voglio piú

b. lei è molto gentile

c. prego, entri e si sieda

2. ....

a. che Giacomo sia il figlio del signor Fini

b. che Giacomo abbia bisogno del suo aiuto

c. che tutti gli abbiano parlato di Giacomo

3. ....

a. avrei bisogno del Suo aiuto

b. me lo dicono tutti

c. ma come fa a saperlo?

4. ....

a. il padre di Giacomo gli ha telefonato

b. Giacomo assomiglia molto a suo padre

c. il direttore ha parlato con il padre di Giacomo

NAME ______________________________ DATE ____________ CLASS ___________

5. ....

a. molto severe

b. non sono conosciute

c. ci si può fidare di loro

6. ....

a. Giacomo riscuoterà l'assegno

b. gli porterà la delega al piú presto

c. sarà indulgente con lui

7. ....

a. una delega cioè una lettera di autorizzazione

b. un assegno bancario

c. una dichiarazione in cui si promette qualcosa

8. ....

a. firmare una dichiarazione

b. parlare con il direttore o con l'impiegato

c. portarla al direttore o all' impiegato

INTONATION AND SOUND DISCRIMINATION

A. *Repeat after the speaker the following question and answer pairs. Listen carefully to the speaker's intonation and copy it.*

1. .... 3. .... 5. ....

2. .... 4. ....

B. *Sound discrimination. You will hear six sentences on tape. After listening to each, indicate the one you heard by circling the letter before it. You will hear each sentence twice.*

1. a. Vado spesso in banca.
   b. Vado spesso in barca.

2. a. Sergio non è basso.
   b. Sergio non è grasso.

3. a. La nostra compagna
   b. La nostra campagna

4. a. Non lavoriamo mai di mattina.
   b. Non laviamo mai di mattina.

5. a. Questa gonna è carina.
   b. Questa donna è carina.

6. a. Non è grave.
   b. Non sono brave.

C. *Repeat after the speaker the following general statements beginning with* chi. *Copy the speaker's intonation and notice the construction.*

1. Chi vuole, può telefonarmi.
2. Chi ha bisogno di danaro, può andare in banca.
3. Chi ha una casa libera, può affittarla.
4. Chi vuole fare un viaggio interessante, può andare in Sicilia.
5. Chi non ha l'ascensore, deve salire le scale a piedi.

PRONUNCIATION

SOUND AND SPELLING OF /f/ AND /v/

A. *The consonants /f/ and /v/ are pronounced as in English.*

Repeat: vena fame fino vale volo foto

favola alveare vuota fumo neve

nove infine tifa refe Rufolo

B. *The spelling of both /f/ and /v/ follows the general rule. The letter* f *or* v *will be doubled when either sound is uttered with high intensity. Remember to pronounce all short vowels in unstressed syllables distinctly, with the same pronunciation as long vowels in stressed syllables.*

Repeat the following pairs of words contrasting low-energy and high-energy /f/ or /v/. They will be repeated after you so that you can check your pronunciation.

rifa/riffa tufo/tuffo intrufola/truffa

afa/affare cefalo/ceffone ciufulo/ciuffo

ove/ovvero bavero/davvero avere/avviene

avola/avvolgere povero/provvedo uovo/ovvio

Repeat the following sentences. Each sentence will be read after you so that you can check your pronunciation.

La vela è avvolta fina affetta le uova avvolte nel filo

l'avvocato è avvilito e affaticato si è intrufolato

e ha truffato il signor Fini quel bavero non è

davvero raffinato l'avolo è in vena di favole

la sfinge l'ha svelato

NAME ______________________ DATE ____________ CLASS ____________

C. *Write the following words. Each word will be repeated so that you can check your accuracy.*

______________	______________
______________	______________
______________	______________
______________	______________
______________	______________
______________	______________
______________	

D I C T A T I O N

Write the following sentences. Each sentence will be repeated during the pause so that you can check your accuracy.

1. ______________________________________

____

2. ______________________________________

____

3. ______________________________________

____

4. ______________________________________

____

5. ______________________________________

____

NAME ______________________ DATE ____________ CLASS ____________

UNIT 21
Part One

D I A L O G U E

Listen to the following dialogue.

ALLA FINESTRA

Laura è a casa della signora del terzo piano, la signora Bruni. Laura e la signora Bruni sono affacciate alla finestra.

Signora Bruni: Laura, guarda in quel palazzo di fronte.
Laura: Che c'è?
Signora Bruni: Guarda quella donna che arriva.
Laura: Che ha di strano? Non noto niente di speciale.
Signora Bruni: Ogni giorno la vedo entrare nel portone esattamente alle undici e quarantacinque. Che ore sono adesso?
Laura: Le 11:45.

Now repeat each sentence after the speaker.

G R A M M A T I C A

I. THE INFINITIVE AS A NOUN

A. *Create new sentences by substituting in the base sentence the infinitives supplied.*

1. Example: Non è bene mangiare troppo.
   bere
   Non è bene bere troppo.

....

....

2. Example: Mangiare è necessario.
bere
Bere è necessario.

....

....

B. *Answer the following questions as in the example. Then repeat the correct sentence after the speaker gives it.*

Example: Tu leggi piú che scrivere, vero?
Sí, preferisco il leggere allo scrivere.

1. .... 3. .... 5. ....

2. .... 4. ....

II. PREPOSITIONS AFTER ADJECTIVES

A. *Create new sentences by substituting in the base sentence the adjectives supplied.*

1. Example: Sono contento del mio lavoro.
felice
Sono felice del mio lavoro.

....

....

2. Example: Gianna è pronta a parlare.
bravo
Gianna è brava a parlare.

....

....

3. Example: Questa frutta è facile da mangiare.
difficile
Questa frutta è difficile da mangiare.

....

....

NAME ______________________ DATE ____________ CLASS ____________

B. *Answer the following questions in the negative using the adjectives supplied. Then repeat the correct sentence after the speaker gives it.*

Example: La tua casa è vicina alla piazza?
lontano
No, la mia casa è lontana dalla piazza.

1. ....
2. ....
3. ....
4. ....

II. VERBS OF PERCEPTION: SPECIAL USES OF *SENTIRE* AND *VEDERE*

A. *Restate the following sentences by changing the second verb to an infinitive. Then repeat the correct sentence after the speaker gives it.*

Example: Guardo il professore mentre insegna l'italiano.
Guardo il professore insegnare l'italiano.

1. ....
2. ....
3. ....
4. ....
5. ....

B. *In the following sentences replace the noun after the infinitive with the corresponding pronoun. Then repeat the correct sentence after the speaker gives it.*

Example: Sento parlare la signora.
La sento parlare.

1. ....
2. ....
3. ....
4. ....
5. ....
6. ....

C. *Restate the following sentences as in the example. Then repeat the correct sentence after the speaker gives it.*

Example: La signora parla e io la sento.
Sento la signora parlare.

1. ....
2. ....
3. ....
4. ....
5. ....
6. ....

III. THE PRONOUN *LO*

A. *Answer the following questions affirmatively using* lo. *Then repeat the correct sentence after the speaker gives it.*

Example: Sei uno studente?
Sì, lo sono.

1. .... 3. .... 5. ....

2. .... 4. ....

B. *Change the following sentences: replace the clause or phrase after the verb with* lo. *Then repeat the correct sentence during the second pause.*

Example: Spero che torni domani.
Lo spero.

1. .... 3. .... 5. ....

2. .... 4. .... 6. ....

Example: È uno studente di musica.
Lo è.

1. .... 3. .... 5. ....

2. .... 4. ....

NAME ______________________ DATE ____________ CLASS ____________

UNIT 21

Part Two

G R A M M A T I C A

MORE USES OF *FARE*

A. *Create new sentences by substituting in the base sentence the subjects supplied.*

1. Example: Che ci facciamo con una macchina da corsa?
   voi
   Che ci fate con una macchina da corsa?

   ....

   ....

2. Example: Non ce la facevamo mai.
   gli studenti
   Gli studenti non ce la facevano mai.

   ....

   ....

B. *Answer the following questions using the words supplied. Then repeat the correct sentence after the speaker gives it.*

Example: Che cosa farai da grande?
il medico
Da grande forse farò il medico.

1. .... 3. .... 5. ....

2. .... 4. ....

C. *Change the following sentences from singular to plural. Then repeat the correct sentence during the second pause.*

Example: Lo studente ha fatto tardi.
Gli studenti hanno fatto tardi.

1. .... 3. .... 5. ....

2. .... 4. ....

LISTENING/COMPREHENSION

Listen to the following dialogue.

SOGNI DI GLORIA

La signora Bruni va a trovare la signora Verdi, la signora del palazzo di fronte.

Signora Bruni: Sono proprio contenta di averLe telefonato e di averLa conosciuta.
Signora Verdi: Anch'io sono molto contenta che sia venuta. Le dovessi dire la verità: credevo che Lei facesse qualcosa di strano... non so, fosse una spia.
Signora Bruni: Questa sí che è da ridere. Io pensavo la stessa cosa di Lei.
Signora Verdi: Quando si diventa vecchi si perde tempo a fantasticare e si finisce per fare delle sciocchezze.
Signora Bruni: Ma ora abbiamo finito di fare sciocchezze. Ho un'idea.
Signora Verdi: Che idea?
Signora Bruni: Il primo giorno che non fa tanto caldo andiamo a cercare un editore.
Signora Verdi: Un editore? Che ci facciamo con un editore?
Signora Bruni: Cerchiamo di vendergli i nostri racconti.
Signora Verdi: Ma siamo pronte a scrivere un libro? Scrivere un libro giallo non è uno scherzo.
Signora Bruni: Sono sicura che con lo scrivere ci verranno in mente tante persone.
Signora Verdi: Peccato però che non abbiamo mai incontrato una spia, in tutto questo tempo. La vita della spia dev'essere affascinante e romantica.
Signora Bruni: La incontreremo nella nostra fantasia.
Signora Verdi: Sarà interessante provare, e soprattutto vedere se saremo capaci di conquistare l'attenzione dei nostri futuri lettori.
Signora Bruni: Magari farli ridere o piangere.
Signora Verdi: Pensa che continueremo a scrivere romanzi per molti anni finché diventeremo ricche e famose?
Signora Bruni: Perché no? Siamo ricche di idee!
Signora Verdi: Io lo dubito.
Signora Bruni: Sia piú indulgente con la nostra carriera di scrittrici di gialli. Se non lo siamo noi, chi lo sarà?

NAME ______________________ DATE ____________ CLASS ____________

QUESTIONS

You will hear eight questions about the dialogue you have just heard. Indicate the correct answer to each question by circling the letter before it. You will hear each question twice.

1. ....

a. al terzo piano

b. all'ultimo piano

c. nel palazzo di fronte alla signora Bruni

2. ....

a. che facesse qualcosa di strano

b. che era da ridere

c. che avesse detto la verità

3. ....

a. delle sciocchezze della signora Verdi

b. un programma alla televisione

c. di aver fantasticato come la signora Verdi

4. ....

a. si fa difficilmente la spesa

b. si perde tempo a fantasticare

c. ci si sente molto soli

5. ....

a. un editore, per pubblicare i loro racconti

b. un lettore, per leggere i loro racconti

c. una libreria

6. ....

a. libri gialli

b. libri d'amore

c. libri di storia italiana

7. ....

a. non possono scrivere un libro giallo

b. la vita di una spia dev'essere affascinante

c. non è una vita abbastanza romantica

8. ....

a. perché conquisteranno l'attenzione dei futuri lettori

b. perché sono ricche d'idee

c. perché faranno ridere e piangere i loro lettori

INTONATION AND SOUND DISCRIMINATION

A. *Repeat after the speaker the following sentences using* continuare a. *Copy the speaker's intonation.*

1. .... 3. .... 5. ....

2. .... 4. ....

B. *Review of future and conditional. Repeat after the speaker the following sentences using either the future or the conditional tense. Then circle* F *if future,* C *if conditional, and the subject of the verb. You will hear each sentence twice.*

1.	F	C	io	tu	lei/lui	noi	voi	loro
2.	F	C	io	tu	lei/lui	noi	voi	loro
3.	F	C	io	tu	lei/lui	noi	voi	loro
4.	F	C	io	tu	lei/lui	noi	voi	loro
5.	F	C	io	tu	lei/lui	noi	voi	loro
6.	F	C	io	tu	lei/lui	noi	voi	loro
7.	F	C	io	tu	lei/lui	noi	voi	loro
8.	F	C	io	tu	lei/lui	noi	voi	loro

PRONUNCIATION

SOUND AND SPELLING OF /kw/

A. *The consonant* q *is pronounced exactly like* k: /k/. *This consonant is always followed by* /w/ *plus another vowel, except in the word* soqquadro, *where it is followed by another* q.

Repeat: quadro quinto quota quieto questo
pasqua iniquo sequestro aliquota squadrato

B. *The sequence* /kw/ *is usually spelled* qu *when the consonant is uttered with low energy. In a few words* /kw/ *is spelled* cu. *When* /kw/ *is pronounced with high energy, the* q *is doubled only in the word* soqquadro. *In the other high-energy* /kw/ *words a* c *is written before the* qu.

NAME ______________________ DATE __________ CLASS __________

The following words are the most common words spelled with cu *instead of* qu. *Look at them while you repeat them.*

cuore cuoco scuola scuotere riscuotere
percuotere cuocere cuoio proficuo
proficua proficui proficue promiscuo
promiscua promiscui promiscue innocuo
innocua innocui innocue

Repeat the following pairs of words contrasting low and high energy /kw/. *Each pair will be read after you so that you can check your pronunciation.*

sequela/acquerello Aquitania/acquistare
loquace/l'acqua iniquo/acquisito aquila/acquisto

Repeat the following sentences. Each sentence will be read after you so that you can check your pronunciation.

l'inquieto cliente acquistò un quadro quindici cuochi in una cucina riscuote quattro assegni per quattro acquerelli non è squartato quinto ha acquistato del cuoio è tanto loquace quanto innocuo

C. *Write the following words. Each word will be repeated during the pause so that you can check your accuracy.*

______________________ ______________________

______________________ ______________________

______________________ ______________________

______________________ ______________________

______________________ ______________________

______________________ ______________________

______________________ ______________________

D I C T A T I O N

Listen to the following sentences. Write each sentence during the pause. Each sentence will be repeated so that you can check your accuracy.

1. ____

2. ____

3. ____

4. ____

5. ____

6. ____

NAME ______________________ DATE ____________ CLASS ____________

UNIT 22

Part One

DIALOGUE

Listen to the following dialogue.

LA CASA DEL NONNO

Giacomo e Laura visitano la casa di campagna del nonno di Giacomo.

Laura: Quanti figli aveva tuo nonno?
Giacomo: Dieci. Mio nonno è ancora vivo, mia nonna è morta l'anno scorso.
Laura: Dieci? Vuol dire che tu hai nove zii e zie?
Giacomo: Veramente ne ho diciotto se conti tutte le rispettive mogli e i rispettivi mariti.
Laura: E venite tutti in questa casa per le vacanze?
Giacomo: Quando eravamo più piccoli ci venivamo spesso. Ci si divertiva molto con i cugini a esplorare i boschi e le colline.

Now repeat each sentence after the speaker.

GRAMMATICA

I. THE PASSIVE VOICE

A. *Change the following sentences from active to passive. Then repeat the correct sentence after the speaker gives it.*

Example: La nonna cucina la cena.
La cena è cucinata dalla nonna.

1. ....
2. ....
3. ....
4. ....
5. ....

B. *Make the following sentences passive, using the required forms of* venire. *Then repeat the correct sentence after the speaker gives it.*

Example: La nonna cucina la cena.
La cena viene cucinata dalla nonna.

1. .... 3. ....

2. .... 4. ....

C. *Change the following sentences into passive statements of obligation using the required forms of* andare. *Then repeat the correct sentence after the speaker gives it.*

Example: I contadini fanno questo lavoro.
Questo lavoro va fatto dai contadini.

1. .... 3. ....

2. .... 4. ....

D. *Change the following sentences from passive to active. Then repeat the correct sentence after the speaker gives it.*

Example: Gli etruschi furono assimilati dai romani.
I romani assimilarono gli etruschi.

1. .... 3. .... 5. ....

2. .... 4. ....

II. DA + INFINITIVE

A. *Change the following sentences by substituting* da *plus infinitive for* che *plus verb. Then repeat the correct sentence after the speaker gives it.*

Example: Erano cose che dovevano farsi subito.
Erano cose da farsi subito.

1. .... 3. ....

2. .... 4. ....

Example: Erano cose che andavano fatte subito.
Erano cose da fare subito.

1. .... 3. ....

2. .... 4. ....

NAME ______________________ DATE ____________ CLASS ____________

B. *Change the following sentences by substituting* da *plus infinitive for* dovere. *Repeat the correct sentence after the speaker gives it.*

Example: Si dovrebbe studiare questo popolo.
Questo popolo è da studiare.

1. .... 3. .... 5. ....

2. .... 4. ....

III. EXCLAMATIONS

A. *Form exclamations with* che *plus the expressions supplied. Then repeat the exclamation after the speaker gives it.*

Example: bella fortuna
Che bella fortuna!

1. .... 3. .... 5. ....

2. .... 4. ....

B. *Create new sentences by substituting in the base sentence the nouns supplied.*

1. Example: Quanta luce ho visto!
alberi
Quanti alberi ho visto!

....

....

2. Example: Quanta gente c'era!
alberi
Quanti alberi c'erano!

....

....

C. *Change the following sentences into exclamations beginning with* come. *Then repeat the correct sentence after the speaker gives it.*

Example: Questo palazzo è grande.
Com'è grande questo palazzo!

1. .... 3. .... 5. ....

2. .... 4. ....

IV. ADJECTIVES IN *-ANTE* AND *-ENTE*, NOUNS

A. *State in a sentence the meaning of each of the nouns given, using the related verb. Then repeat the correct sentence after the speaker gives it.*

Example: combattente
È una persona che combatte.

1. .... 3. .... 5. ....

2. .... 4. .... 6. ....

B. *Change the following sentences by using nouns ending in* -ante *and* -ente. *Then repeat the correct sentence after the speaker gives it.*

Example: È uno studente che ripete una classe.
È un ripetente.

1. .... 3. .... 5. ....

2. .... 4. .... 6. ....

C. *Change the following sentences as in the example. Then repeat the correct sentence after the speaker gives it.*

Example: Mario è una persona che insiste troppo.
Mario è una persona troppo insistente.

1. .... 3. .... 5. ....

2. .... 4. .... 6. ....

NAME ______________________ DATE ____________ CLASS ____________

UNIT 22

Part Two

SEMBRARE AND PARERE

A. *Create new sentences by substituting in the base sentence the subjects supplied.*

1. Example: L'operaio sembra contento.
   la bambina
   La bambina sembra contenta.

   ....

   ....

2. Example: Il fornaio non pareva soddisfatto.
   gli stranieri
   Gli stranieri non parevano soddisfatti.

   ....

   ....

B. *Create new sentences by substituting in the base sentence the noun objects supplied.*

Example: Quello sembra un palazzo antico.
case nuove
Quelle sembrano delle case nuove.

....

....

C. *Change the following sentences from the present to the imperfect, then to the past absolute. Repeat each correct sentence after the speaker gives it.*

Example: Mi sembra una casa nuova.
Mi sembrava una casa nuova.
Mi sembrò una casa nuova.

1. .... 3. .... 5. ....

2. .... 4. .... 6. ....

LISTENING / COMPREHENSION

Listen to the following dialogue.

GLI ANTENATI DI GIACOMO

Laura e Giacomo parlano degli etruschi, un popolo del passato.

Laura: Ma come? Ci sono delle rovine etrusche nella terra di tuo nonno?
Giacomo: Vieni, te le faccio vedere.
Laura: Perché nessuno viene a scavarle?
Giacomo: In Italia ci sono rovine dappertutto. Queste, come tante altre, non sono state scavate perché non hanno molta importanza storica.
Laura: Se cominciamo a scavare noi, forse troviamo una tomba piena di vasi e gioielli e alle pareti, dei dipinti.
Giacomo: Lo dubito; però è capitato una volta a dei ragazzi che esploravano delle grotte vicino al mare.
Laura: Mi ricordo. Il fatto è stato riportato sul giornale.
Giacomo: Già, perché le tombe venivano allestite come se fossero delle vere e proprie case.
Laura: Lo sai che assomigli alle statue etrusche che si trovano al museo?
Giacomo: La cosa non mi meraviglia. Una buona parte dell'Umbria era abitata dal popolo etrusco prima della conquista dei romani.
Laura: La loro civiltà è scomparsa completamente, non è vero?
Giacomo: No, non completamente. Più che scomparire o essere distrutti, gli etruschi furono assimilati dal popolo vincente man mano che le loro città venivano conquistate.
Laura: Dovevano essere felici, a giudicare dal sorriso che molte statue hanno sulle labbra.
Giacomo: Era gente misteriosa di cui sappiamo poco. Forse una gente da ammirare. Sembra fosse un popolo pacifico e non aggressivo come quello romano.
Laura: Certamente un popolo da studiare. Un volta che la loro scrittura sarà non solo decifrata ma capita, sapremo molto di più sui loro costumi e le loro origini.

NAME ______________________________ DATE ____________ CLASS ____________

QUESTIONS

You will hear seven questions about the dialogue you have just heard. Indicate the correct answer to each question by circling the letter before it. Each question will be repeated twice.

1. ....

   a. delle rovine etrusche

   b. la casa dove abita il nonno

   c. delle costruzioni moderne che hanno importanza storica

2. ....

   a. sono piene di vasi e gioielli

   b. non hanno molta importanza storica

   c. Giacomo le fa vedere a Laura

3. ....

   a. di trovare una tomba piena di dipinti

   b. di trovare una grotta

   c. di esplorare delle grotte vicino al mare

4. ....

   a. a suo padre

   b. a suo nonno

   c. alle statue etrusche che sono al museo

5. ....

   a. nel museo etrusco

   b. in una buona parte dell'Umbria

   c. in Sicilia

6. ....

   a. molte statue hanno il sorriso sulle labbra

   b. non sappiamo molto della loro civiltà

   c. era gente misteriosa

7. ....

   a. gli etruschi erano pacifici come i romani

   b. gli etruschi erano aggressivi come i romani

   c. gli etruschi erano un popolo pacifico e non aggressivo

INTONATION AND SOUND DISCRIMINATION

A. *Repeat after the speaker the following exclamations. Copy the intonation and speak with energy.*

1. ....   4. ....   7. ....

2. ....   5. ....   8. ....

3. ....   6. ....

B. *Sound discrimination. You will hear six sentences on tape. After listening to each, indicate the one you heard by circling the letter before it. You will hear each sentence twice.*

1. a. Hanno una bella cucina.
   b. Hanno una bella cugina.

2. a. Laura non pensa molto.
   b. Laura non pesa molto.

3. a. Ecco la porta!
   b. Ecco la torta!

4. a. Non l'hanno trovato.
   b. Non l'hanno provato.

5. a. Ci vediamo alle sette.
   b. Ci andiamo alle sette.

6. a. Ha pochi capelli.
   b. Ha pochi cappelli.

C. *Review of past absolute. Listen to the following sentences using the past absolute tense. Repeat each after the speaker, then circle the subject of the verb. You will hear each sentence twice.*

1. .... io tu lei/lui noi voi loro

2. .... io tu lei/lui noi voi loro

3. .... io tu lei/lui noi voi loro

4. .... io tu lei/lui noi voi loro

5. .... io tu lei/lui noi voi loro

6. .... io tu lei/lui noi voi loro

7. .... io tu lei/lui noi voi loro

NAME ______________________ DATE ____________ CLASS __________

PRONUNCIATION

SOUND AND SPELLING OF /ts/ AND /dz/

A. *The consonant which is written in Italian as* z *has two sounds:* /ts/ *and* /dz/. *Both of these sounds are heard in English (though neither is written as* z) *in, for example,* cats *and* gods.

The sound /ts/ *always occurs when* z *appears before the diphthongs* /io/, /ia/, /ie/; *at times when it is preceded by* l, n, *or* r; *and at times when it is doubled. There is no way of knowing from the spelling whether a* z *is pronounced* /ts/ *or* /dz/ *when it follows* l, n, *or* r, *or when it is doubled.*

Repeat: stazione marziano spezie lezioso

marzo scorza alzo balzo forza

lenza lonza

Repeat the following pairs of words in which low and high energy /ts/ *are contrasted. Each pair will be read after you so that you can check your pronunciation.*

dazio/ragazzo spezia/razza ozio/mozzo

sazio/spazzola

B. *The sound* /dz/ *occurs when* z *appears at the beginning of a word; at times when it is preceded by* l, n, *or* r; *and at times when it is doubled.*

Repeat: zucchero zolla zero Zara zita

zeta zoo zoccolo gonzo manzo

inzuppare Monza marzapane orzillo elzeviro

Repeat the following words which have high-energy /dz/ *and in which a double* z *appears. Each word will be read after you so that you can check your pronunciation.*

razzo azzimato azzerare mezzo uzzolo

buzzurro azzurro bozzima

Repeat the following phrases. Each phrase will be read after you so you can check your pronunciation.

una zolletta di zucchero una zebra nello zoo

un ragazzo azzimato è un razzo azzurro l'ozio è il

padre dei vizi non è sazio di Venezia quel buzzurro

è zoppo

C. *Write the following words. Each word will be repeated so that you can check your accuracy.*

______________	______________
______________	______________
______________	______________
______________	______________
______________	______________
______________	

DICTATION

Write the following sentences. Each sentence will be read twice so that you can check your accuracy.

1. ____

____

2. ____

____

3. ____

____

4. ____

____

5. ____

____